diabetes
BREAKTHROUGHS
2009

178 RECIPES TO SATISFY YOUR SWEET TOOTH WITHOUT GUILT

DECADENT
DESSERTS

FROM THE EDITORS OF **Prevention**®

RODALE

This book is intended as a reference volume only, not as a medical manual. Keep in mind that nutritional needs vary from person to person, depending upon age, sex, health status, and total diet. The foods discussed and the recipes given here are designed to help you make informed decisions about your diet and health.

Printed in the United States of America
Rodale Inc. makes every effort to use acid-free ∞, recycled paper ♻ .

Interior Photographs by Rodale Images
© Rodale Images: pages 61, 67 (shortcake), 144, 145, 150, 151, 152
© Mitch Mandel/Rodale Images: pages 62, 63, 64, 65, 67 (coffee cake), 69, 71, 72, 73, 74, 76, 141, 143, 146, 147, 148, 149, 153, 154, 155
© Kurt Wilson/Rodale Images: pages 66, 68, 75, 156
© Tad Ware & Company Inc./ Rodale Images: pages 70, 142
Book design by Nancy Smola Biltcliff

ISBN 13: 978–1–60529–886–3
ISBN 10: 1–60529–886–7

2 4 6 8 10 9 7 5 3 1 hardcover

We inspire and enable people to improve their lives and the world around them
For more of our products visit **rodalestore.com** or call 800-848-4735

Contents

In all Rodale cookbooks, our mission is to provide delicious and nutritious recipes. Our recipes also meet the standards of the Rodale Test Kitchen for dependability, ease, practicality, and, most of all, great taste. To give us your comments, call (800) 848-4735.

Breaking *the* Dessert Myth

I know what you're thinking. Diabetes and desserts just don't seem to go together. But can you imagine the rest of your life without treats? Well, you don't have to! The good news is that you *can* have sugar!

For years, people with diabetes were taught to avoid concentrated sweets, known as simple sugars, because they were thought to overload the blood with glucose much faster than starches (complex carbohydrates). Diet plans to control diabetes consisted of two phrases: "avoid sugar" and "lose weight."

But finally things are changing. Research from the American Diabetes Association now shows that there's no need to eliminate sugar totally. Many research studies completed over the past 20 years have demonstrated that foods containing sugar can be part of a healthy diet, even for people with diabetes.

This is because it's not just sugar, but all carbohydrates, that can affect blood sugar levels. In turn, this means that baked potatoes and pasta are as likely to raise sugar levels as cakes and cookies. No longer are diabetics being told to avoid sugar completely. Besides, it would be an almost impossible task because many healthy foods contain some form of sugar. So for the almost 24 million Americans who have diabetes, that occasional snacking on a cookie won't harm them when it is included as part of a healthy meal plan.

The optimal diet choice for diabetics is counting grams of carbohydrates, not grams of sugar. The total grams of carbohydrates being consumed vary from person to person, depending on their weight, activity level, and whether they inject insulin. Everything, from fruits and desserts to grains and dairy, should be included in this daily count.

This system widens meal options for many diabetics who feared that creamy, sugary desserts would shock their bodies. Of course, there may be healthier options than a slice of cake, but, in the long run, treating yourself to dessert now and then is more likely to keep the rest of your diet on track.

What's the Best Way to Eat If I Have Diabetes?

Even if you have diabetes, you can have your cake and eat it too. The key is to integrate desserts into an overall healthy diet. What you eat and, in some cases, what you don't is at the heart of any treatment plan. Along with regular exercise, eating right helps keep blood sugar and triglycerides at steady levels, which is the key to keeping problems under control.

Another reason to eat right? "Being overweight is clearly your biggest modifiable diabetes risk factor," says Harvard researcher Caren G. Solomon, MD. "First and foremost, you need to control the amount you eat. But that doesn't mean you can just cut your calories down to 1,200 and eat anything you like."

That said, it's important to balance out what you eat so you can fit desserts into your life. Keep the following guidelines in mind when you plan your meals.

Step 1
Eat nine servings of vegetables and fruits every day.

Veggies and fruits should be the foundation of your diet—as opposed to grains, the foundation of the traditional Food Guide Pyramid. You'll be eating nine ½-cup servings of a variety of fruits and veggies a day. Sound like overkill? In reality, it could spell extra life. Study after study links diets highest in fruits and vegetables with less diabetes and many other diseases. More and more experts are saying that five a day should be the minimum and that nine a day—five vegetables and four fruits—is the optimum. Yet most Americans get only four servings total a day.

Step 2
Eat three to six whole grain foods every day.

Diets high in whole grains are linked to less diabetes as well as heart disease, stroke, and cancer. If you've been eating a high-carbohydrate diet with lots of refined grains—typically breads, rolls, bagels, pretzels, crackers, and pizza made from white flour—it may be a challenge at first to find whole grain substitutes.

But the payoff is worth it. To your body, refined white flour is the same as sugar, making a diet high in white-flour foods the same as a high-sugar diet.

Whole grains also mean extra fiber, which is the closest thing to a magic bullet for weight loss. It not only fills you up quickly with fewer calories, but also eliminates some of the calories you eat!

To maximize fiber's healing powers, aim for 25 to 35 grams a day.

Step 3
Eat two or three calcium-rich foods every day.

This is great advice for everyone, not just for people with diabetes. Not only does adequate calcium support strong bones and help prevent osteoporosis, but clinical studies suggest that it also helps prevent colon cancer, high blood pressure, and PMS. And calcium may lower your body fat. A group of women who consumed at least 1,000 milligrams of calcium a day, along with a diet of no more than 1,900 calories, lost more weight—as much as 6 pounds more—during a 2-year study than women who ate less calcium.

Obvious high-calcium choices include 1% and fat-free milk, low-fat and fat-free yogurt, and reduced-fat and fat-free cheese. Other good choices are calcium-fortified orange and grapefruit juices and soy milk. To equal the calcium found in milk, look for at least 30 percent of the Daily Value for calcium per serving.

Step 4
Eat beans at least five times a week.

Beans are the highest-fiber foods you can find, with the single exception of breakfast cereals made with wheat bran. Diets high in fiber are linked to less diabetes and other chronic diseases. When using canned beans, rinse and drain them to remove as much as one-third of the added sodium.

Step 5
Nosh on nuts five times a week.

Studies show that people who eat nuts regularly have less heart disease and other illness than people who avoid them. (People with diabetes are at increased risk of heart disease.) Even among the healthiest eaters, the ones who also eat nuts have the best health record. Exactly why isn't known yet, but one reason could be compounds in nuts called tocotrienols.

The key to eating nuts is not to eat too many; they're so high in calories that you could easily gain weight. To avoid temptation, I suggest keeping a jar of chopped nuts in your fridge. Sprinkle 2 tablespoons a day on cereal, yogurt, veggies, salads, or wherever the crunch and rich flavor appeal to you.

Step 6
Feast on fish.

Studies show that people who eat fish twice a week have fewer fatal heart attacks. Scientists credit omega-3 fats, which have the ability to prevent the development of a dangerously irregular heartbeat.

The protein in fish is also a great hunger-stopper, and it helps build healthy muscles that burn tons of calories. "Fish is an excellent source of protein because it's high in omega-3 fatty acids that are good for your heart while low in cholesterol and saturated fat," says Michael Hamilton, MD, MPH, former program and medical director of the Diet and Fitness Center at Duke University in Durham, North Carolina. "And protein is important for promoting satiety—the feeling of fullness you look for from a meal." To get the most omega-3s, choose salmon, white albacore tuna canned in water, rainbow trout, anchovies, herring, sardines, or mackerel.

Step 7
Drink eight glasses of water every day, plus a cup or more of tea.

Every cell in your body needs water to function. Not only does drinking lots of water help you feel full, but big water drinkers also appear to get less colon and bladder cancer. Every cup of tea you drink provides a strong infusion of antioxidants that help to keep blood from clotting too easily (which may thwart heart attacks). Antioxidants also may help lower your risk of cancer and rheumatoid arthritis.

Step 8
Keep your fat budget.

To stay within a healthy fat budget—25 percent of calories from fat—first you must find the maximum fat allowance for your calorie level.

When you follow a diet that emphasizes these healthy eating patterns, saving room for dessert a few times per week is a great way to keep balance in your diet.

How to Add Desserts Back into Your Life

After being diagnosed with diabetes, you may have shunned desserts, but that is not necessary. We have learned that sugar has about the same effect on blood glucose as any other carbohydrate. Therefore, using sugar as part of the total carbohydrate content of the diet is okay for people with diabetes. Just make sure to substitute these sugar-containing foods for other carbohydrate choices as part of a balanced meal plan. Nutrition therapy is not about avoiding sugar, but rather about controlling blood glucose.

Talk to your doctor or a registered dietitian if you'd like to incorporate sweets into your diet. In general, it's a good idea to avoid too many high-sugar foods. They offer lots of empty calories and not much else. But dessert several times a week is possible.

How to Add Sugar to Your Diet

• Use sugar as part of your total carbohydrate intake. This does not mean you should eat unlimited amounts of sugar or dessert foods, but rather you should eat these foods in moderation because most high-sugar foods have little nutritional value. The good news is that totally eliminating sugar is unnecessary. In fact, it's impossible. There are small amounts of naturally occurring sugars in two very healthy foods: fruit and milk.

• Read food labels to determine how much of the carbohydrate comes from sugar and if the food is nutritious or just an empty-calorie item.

• If you eat a high-sugar food, use the serving size as your guide. Most average-size cookies list one or two cookies as a serving size; ice creams list ½ cup. Most people eat at least twice that much. Be sure to divide the recipes in this book into the stated number of servings.

• Be sensible—but enjoy your new food choices. It is not "cheating" to eat foods that contain sugar as long as your meals are within the context of healthy eating. You're not a bad person for enjoying all foods. You're a normal person who happens to have diabetes, living in the real world.

• Use the dessert recipes we've chosen for you in this book. To give you the most bang for your buck, we've created recipes that provide the most healthful version of your favorite dessert using the least amount of sugar.

Finding the Sugar Content

One way to find sugar in foods is to look at the food label. In the nutrition facts section, check the "sugar" category. If you look in the ingredients list, the sugars in the product are listed individually, but they're often listed under names that most consumers do not recognize as sugars.

The following list gives some of the obvious and not-so-obvious sugar names to look for: brown sugar, confectioners' sugar, carob, corn syrup, dextrose, fructose, galactose, glucose, honey, invert sugar, lactose, maltose, maple syrup, molasses, sucrose, and turbinado.

Simple Ways to Make Desserts Diabetes-Friendly

When you have diabetes, your nutrition goals should include eating low-fat, low-cholesterol foods. No doubt, some of your favorite dessert recipes don't exactly fit that bill. But they can—with just an easy change or two! Whether it's an ingredient substitution or a different preparation technique, the result can taste better than you ever would have imagined. Just try some of the ideas here. We're sure you'll become a believer! Best of all, you'll feel really good knowing that you're taking care of your diabetes while you're enjoying great food!

Cakes and Quick Breads

Whip up good texture. The advantage of baking with butter or shortening is that air pockets are formed when these ingredients are creamed with sugar. This is what makes the finished product light and tender. You can get similar effects by whipping sugar with egg whites. This will give lightness and tenderness without the fat of butter or shortening.

Try fruit puree instead of butter. An easy way to cut back on butter or shortening is to replace it with an equal amount of fruit puree. In most recipes, you can replace up to half the fat with puree without noticing the difference.

When making chocolate desserts, prune puree is ideal. Soften pitted prunes briefly in hot water, drain, and blend in a food processor until smooth. Or use baby food prunes.

Use low-fat dairy products. Cakes contain a number of ingredients that often can be replaced with low-fat or even fat-free equivalents, with essentially no change in the resulting taste or texture.

- Replace whole milk with fat-free, 1%, or 2% milk.
- Substitute buttermilk, low-fat or fat-free plain yogurt, or low-fat sour cream for regular sour cream.
- Replace full-fat cream cheese with its low-fat counterpart.

• Replace chocolate with cocoa. When you want the full, rich taste of chocolate without all the saturated fat, try using unsweetened cocoa powder. Cocoa contains only a small amount of fat, yet it still packs a big punch of chocolate flavor.

• For every ounce of melted unsweetened chocolate, substitute 3 tablespoons of cocoa powder dissolved in 2 tablespoons of warm water and mixed with 1 tablespoon of prune puree.

• When using cocoa, dissolving it first in warm water helps the cocoa flavor bloom, making it more intense.

• To use cocoa to replace semisweet chocolate, add 3 to 5 table-spoons of sugar to help keep the sweetness in balance.

Cookies and Bars

Melt the butter. You can reduce the amount of butter in a recipe by about half if you melt it before adding it to the other ingredients. Essentially, this makes the butter go further, which helps cookies to bake up properly, despite the lower amount of fat.

Use fruit in place of butter. Another way to reduce the amount of butter or other fat is to replace ½ cup of it with an equal amount of apple-sauce or another fruit puree.

Go easy on the chocolate chips. Chocolate chips have a fair amount of fat and sugar. You can often cut back on them without adversely affecting the recipe.

• Substitute miniature chocolate chips for the full-size kind. It will taste like you're getting more chocolate than you actually are.

• Replace some of the chocolate chips with dried apricots, raisins, or chopped dates.

Change your flour. Substituting whole grain pastry flour for all-purpose white flour adds fiber, vitamins, and minerals, while maintaining the cookies' tender texture.

Pies and Tarts

Reduce the saturated fats. Many of the recipes in this book are prepared with half butter and half canola oil, giving you less saturated fat than an all-butter or all-shortening crust contains.

Go for cookie crusts. Crusts made by using low-fat cookies, such as graham crackers or gingersnaps, are a healthier alternative to a rolled pie crust.

Cobblers and Crisps

Pump up the oats. Adding rolled oats to toppings increases the fiber of the recipe. Oats also add a nutty flavor and texture to these fruit-based desserts.

Cakes *and* Quick Breads

The world's earliest bakers began making cakes and breads around 4000 BC, shortly after the invention of flour. Back then, cakes were described as flour-based sweet foods, while breads were simply flour-based foods. This chapter contains cakes and quick breads that have come a long way from both those of the primitive people and from the high-fat, high-sugar versions you are used to seeing. All-fruit preserves replace traditional sugary syrups and icings, making them better for you. Whole grain pastry flour and reduced-fat dairy products such as yogurt, sour cream, and milk help them to keep their light, fluffy texture.

Almond-Chocolate Flourless Cake

3   *tablespoons unsweetened cocoa powder*

½   *cup blanched almonds*

2   *tablespoons + ¾ cup sugar*

3   *ounces bittersweet chocolate, chopped*

½   *cup reduced-fat sour cream*

2   *large egg yolks, at room temperature*

1   *tablespoon butter*

1   *teaspoon vanilla extract*

¼   *teaspoon almond extract (optional)*

5   *large egg whites, at room temperature*

¼   *teaspoon salt*

1   *tablespoon toasted slivered almonds (optional)*

Preheat the oven to 350°F. Coat a 9" springform pan with cooking spray. Dust with 1 tablespoon of the cocoa powder.

In a food processor, combine the blanched almonds and 2 tablespoons of the sugar. Pulse until finely ground.

Place the chocolate in a large microwaveable bowl. Microwave on high power for 1 minute. Stir until smooth; if necessary, microwave for a few more seconds to melt completely. Stir in the ground almonds, sour cream, egg yolks, butter, vanilla extract, almond extract (if using), ½ cup of the remaining sugar, and the remaining 2 tablespoons cocoa powder.

Place the egg whites and salt in a large bowl. Using an electric mixer on high speed, beat until soft peaks form. Gradually beat in the remaining ¼ cup sugar until stiff, glossy peaks form.

Gently stir one-quarter of the egg whites into the chocolate mixture to lighten it. Fold in the remaining whites until no white streaks remain. Pour into the prepared pan and smooth the top.

Bake for 30 minutes, or until a wooden pick inserted in the center comes out with just a few moist crumbs.

Cool on a rack. The cake will fall as it cools, leaving a raised edge. Gently press down the edge as it cools. Remove the pan sides and place on a serving plate. Sprinkle with the toasted almonds (if using).

Makes 12 servings

Per serving: 171 calories, 4 g protein, 21 g carbohydrates, 9 g fat, 3 g saturated fat, 40 mg cholesterol, 40 mg sodium, 2 g dietary fiber

Exchanges: 1½ other carbohydrate, ½ lean meat, 1½ fat

Rich Chocolate Layer Cake

Cake

Photograph
on page 66

1½	*cups whole grain pastry flour*
½	*cup unsweetened cocoa powder*
1	*tablespoon instant espresso powder*
1	*teaspoon baking soda*
8	*tablespoons butter, softened*
1	*cup sugar*
1	*egg*
1	*teaspoon vanilla extract*
½	*cup low-fat buttermilk*
½	*cup hot tap water*

Frosting

1½	*cups sugar*
¼	*cup water*
3	*egg whites, at room temperature*
1	*teaspoon cream of tartar*
1	*teaspoon vanilla extract*
¼	*cup unsweetened cocoa powder*

To make the cake: Preheat the oven to 350°F. Coat two 8" round cake pans with cooking spray.

In a medium bowl, mix the flour, cocoa powder, espresso powder, and baking soda.

Place the butter and sugar in a large bowl. Using an electric mixer on medium speed, beat for 3 minutes, or until creamy. Add the egg and vanilla extract. Beat on low speed until creamy.

With the mixer on low speed, beat in one-third of the flour mixture and the buttermilk. Beat in half of the remaining flour mixture and the water. Beat in the remaining flour mixture. Pour into the prepared pans.

Bake for 25 minutes, or until a wooden pick inserted in the center comes out clean. Cool on a rack for 10 minutes. Remove from the pans and place on the rack to cool completely.

To make the frosting: In the top of a double boiler, mix the sugar, water, egg whites, and cream of tartar. Place over a saucepan of simmering water. With clean beaters and the mixer on high speed, beat for 5 minutes, or until soft peaks form. Add the vanilla extract and beat for 4 minutes, or until the mixture is thick and glossy and registers 160°F on an instant-read thermometer. Remove from the heat.

Sift the cocoa powder over the frosting and gently fold in. Allow to cool completely, about 20 minutes.

Place 1 cooled cake layer on a serving plate. Evenly spread the top with frosting. Top with the remaining cake layer and spread the top with frosting. Spread the remaining frosting over the sides.

Makes 16 servings

Per serving: 222 calories, 3 g protein, 40 g carbohydrates, 7 g fat, 4 g saturated fat, 29 mg cholesterol, 160 mg sodium, 2 g dietary fiber

Exchanges: ½ starch, 2 other carbohydrate, 1 fat

Chocolate Avalanche Cake

Photograph on page 62

1¾   cups whole grain pastry flour

1   cup sugar

½   cup unsweetened cocoa powder

1   teaspoon baking powder

½   teaspoon baking soda

¼   teaspoon salt

1½   cups (12 ounces) low-fat plain yogurt

2   tablespoons canola oil

1   teaspoon vanilla extract

3   egg whites, at room temperature

1¼   cups raspberries

2   tablespoons honey

2   tablespoons hot tap water

¼   cup raspberry all-fruit preserves, melted

Preheat the oven to 350°F. Coat a 9" x 9" baking dish with cooking spray.

In a large bowl, mix the flour, ½ cup of the sugar, ¼ cup of the cocoa powder, the baking powder, baking soda, and salt.

In a small bowl, mix 1 cup of the yogurt, the oil, and vanilla extract.

Place the egg whites in a medium bowl. Using an electric mixer on high speed, beat until soft peaks form. Gradually beat in the remaining ½ cup sugar until stiff, glossy peaks form.

Stir the yogurt mixture into the flour mixture just until moistened. Fold in the egg whites until no streaks of white remain.

Pour into the prepared baking dish. Sprinkle evenly with 1 cup of the raspberries.

Bake for 40 minutes, or until a wooden pick inserted in the center comes out clean. Cool on a rack for 10 minutes. Remove from the pan and place on the rack to cool completely.

In a small bowl, mix the honey, water, and the remaining ¼ cup cocoa powder.

In another small bowl, mix the preserves and the remaining ½ cup yogurt.

To serve, cut the cake into squares and top with a dollop of yogurt and a drizzle of chocolate sauce (see page 218). Garnish with the remaining ¼ cup raspberries.

Makes 12 servings

Per serving: 195 calories, 5 g protein, 39 g carbohydrates, 4 g fat, 1 g saturated fat, 3 mg cholesterol, 170 mg sodium, 3 g dietary fiber

Exchanges: 1 starch, 1½ other carbohydrate, 1 fat

Chocolate-Raspberry Cake

Photograph
on page 68

1	cup whole grain pastry flour
½	cup sugar
3	tablespoons unsweetened cocoa powder
1	teaspoon baking powder
¼	teaspoon salt
1	cup (8 ounces) low-fat vanilla yogurt
2	tablespoons canola oil
2	egg yolks, at room temperature
1	teaspoon vanilla extract
2	large egg whites, at room temperature
1¼	cups reduced-fat whipped topping
1½	cups raspberries
½	cup raspberry all-fruit preserves, melted
	Mint sprigs (optional)

Preheat the oven to 350°F. Coat an 8" round baking pan with cooking spray.

In a medium bowl, mix the flour, sugar, cocoa powder, baking powder, and salt.

In a large bowl, mix the yogurt, oil, egg yolks, and vanilla extract.

Place the egg whites in a medium bowl. Using an electric mixer on high speed, beat until stiff peaks form.

Stir the flour mixture into the yogurt mixture just until blended. Fold in the egg whites until no streaks of white remain. Pour into the prepared pan.

Bake for 35 minutes, or until a wooden pick inserted in the center comes out clean. Cool on a rack for 5 minutes. Remove from the pan and place on the rack to cool completely.

To serve, split the cake horizontally into 2 layers. Spread 1 cup of the whipped topping over 1 layer. Top with 1 cup of the raspberries and drizzle with the preserves. Top with the remaining cake layer and spoon 12 dollops of the remaining whipped topping around the cake. Top each with a few of the remaining raspberries and garnish with the mint (if using).

Makes 12 servings

Per serving: 161 calories, 4 g protein, 27 g carbohydrates, 5 g fat, 2 g saturated fat, 35 mg cholesterol, 115 mg sodium, 3 g dietary fiber

Exchanges: 1 other starch, 1 fat

Angel Food Cake

1	cup + 2 tablespoons sifted cake flour
1¼	cups + 2 tablespoons sugar
12	egg whites, at room temperature
1¼	teaspoons cream of tartar
¼	teaspoon salt
½	teaspoon almond extract
1½	teaspoons vanilla extract

Preheat the oven to 350°F.

Sift the flour with ½ cup of the sugar three times. Set aside.

In a clean and dry large bowl, combine the egg whites, cream of tartar, and salt. Using an electric mixer on high speed, beat until the egg whites form soft peaks. Gradually beat in the remaining sugar, ¼ cup at a time. Add the almond extract and vanilla extract. Beat until glossy.

Gently fold the flour mixture into the egg-white mixture in 3 stages, folding just enough to mix each time. Gently pour the batter into an ungreased 9" or 10" straight-sided nonstick tube pan and smooth the surface of the batter evenly.

Bake for 40 to 45 minutes, or until the cake is golden brown. Invert the pan over the top of a heavy long-necked bottle or funnel and let cool for 1½ to 2 hours. Gently remove to a serving platter.

Makes 12 servings

Per serving: 243 calories, 5 g protein, 56 g carbohydrates, 1 g fat, 0 g saturated fat, 0 mg cholesterol, 104 mg sodium, 1 g dietary fiber

Exchanges: ½ starch, 2½ other carbohydrate, ½ very lean meat

Variation

For a colorful angelfood cake, fold 3 to 4 tablespoons colored crystal sprinkles into the batter with the last addition of flour.

Per serving: 247 calories, 5 g protein, 57 g carbohydrates, 1 g fat, 0 g saturated fat, 0 mg cholesterol, 104 mg sodium, 1 g dietary fiber

Exchanges: ½ starch, 2½ other carbohydrate, ½ very lean meat

Yummy Pineapple Cake

1 package (18 ounces) yellow cake mix
¾ cup liquid egg substitute or 3 eggs
1 cup water
1 can (20 ounces) crushed pineapple in juice
8 ounces fat-free cream cheese, at room temperature
2 cups fat-free milk
1 package (4-serving-size) sugar-free instant vanilla pudding mix
⅛ teaspoon ground cinnamon
1 cup reduced-fat whipped topping
1 can (15½ ounces) mandarin oranges, drained (optional)

Preheat the oven to 325°F, or according to the cake mix package directions. Coat a 13" x 9" baking dish with cooking spray.

Prepare the cake mix according to the package directions, using the egg substitute or eggs and water. Pour into the prepared baking dish.

Bake according to the package directions. Cool on a rack.

Poke holes all over the cake with a fork or the handle of a teaspoon. Pour the pineapple (with juice) over the cake.

Place the cream cheese in a large bowl. Using an electric mixer on medium speed, beat until smooth. Add the milk, pudding mix, and cinnamon. Beat for 3 minutes. Pour over the pineapple. Top with the whipped topping. Decorate with the oranges (if using). Cover and refrigerate for at least 4 hours.

Makes 12 servings

Per serving: 283 calories, 8 g protein, 45 g carbohydrates, 9 g fat, 4 g saturated fat, 60 mg cholesterol, 480 mg sodium, 1 g dietary fiber

Exchanges: ½ milk, 2½ other carbohydrate, ½ lean meat, 1 fat

Peach Upside-Down Cake

⅔   cup sugar

2   tablespoons butter, at room temperature

2½   pounds large ripe peaches, peeled, halved, and pitted

1   cup whole grain pastry flour

1   teaspoon baking powder

½   teaspoon baking soda

½   teaspoon ground cinnamon

¼   teaspoon salt

1   tablespoon canola oil

1   egg

1   teaspoon vanilla extract

1   teaspoon almond extract

½   cup low-fat buttermilk

Preheat the oven to 375°F.

In a 9" cast-iron skillet, combine ⅓ cup of the sugar and 1 tablespoon of the butter. Cook over medium heat for 3 to 5 minutes, or until the sugar begins to melt. Add the peaches, cut side up, in a single layer. (The fruit should fit tightly.) Remove from the heat.

In a medium bowl, mix the flour, baking powder, baking soda, cinnamon, and salt.

Place the oil, the remaining ⅓ cup sugar, and the remaining 1 tablespoon butter in a large bowl. Using an electric mixer on medium speed, beat until smooth. Add the egg, vanilla extract, and almond extract. Beat until smooth.

With the mixer on low speed, add the buttermilk and the flour mixture, beating just until incorporated. Spoon evenly over the peaches in the skillet.

Bake for 20 to 25 minutes, or until a wooden pick inserted in the center comes out clean.

Cool on a rack for 5 minutes. Loosen the edges of the cake with a knife. Invert the cake onto a serving plate. If any of the peaches stick to the skillet, remove them with a knife and replace them on the cake.

Makes 8 servings

Per serving: 219 calories, 4 g protein, 42 g carbohydrates, 6 g fat, 2 g saturated fat, 35 mg cholesterol, 270 mg sodium, 4 g dietary fiber

Exchanges: ½ starch, 1 fruit, 1½ other carbohydrate, 1 fat

Strawberry Cream Cake

Photograph on page 63

¾	cup sifted whole grain pastry flour
¾	cup sifted oat flour
1	tablespoon baking powder
3	egg whites, at room temperature
8	tablespoons butter, at room temperature
¼	cup packed light brown sugar
¼	cup granulated sugar
2	egg yolks
¾	cup 2% milk, at room temperature
1	teaspoon vanilla extract
¼	cup strawberry all-fruit preserves, melted
1½	cups reduced-fat whipped topping
1	pint strawberries, sliced

Preheat the oven to 350°F. Coat an 8" round cake pan with cooking spray. Dust with flour.

In a small bowl, mix the pastry flour, oat flour, and baking powder.

Place the egg whites in a large bowl. Using an electric mixer on high speed, beat until stiff peaks form.

In another large bowl, beat the butter, brown sugar, and granulated sugar on medium speed for 2 minutes, or until creamy. Add the egg yolks, one at a time, and beat for 4 minutes, or until fluffy.

Beat in one-third of the flour mixture and one-half of the milk. Repeat, beginning and ending with the flour. Beat in the vanilla extract.

Gently fold one-third of the egg whites into the yolk mixture. Fold in the remaining whites until no streaks of white remain. Pour into the prepared pan.

Bake for 35 minutes, or until a wooden pick inserted in the center comes out clean. Cool on a rack for 10 minutes. Remove from the pan and place on the rack to cool completely.

To serve, split the cooled cake horizontally into 2 layers. Spread half of the preserves over the bottom layer. Cover with half of the whipped topping and half of the strawberries. Top with the remaining layer and coat with the remaining preserves and whipped topping. Arrange the remaining strawberries over the top.

Makes 10 servings

Per serving: 273 calories, 5 g protein, 24 g carbohydrates, 18 g fat, 10 g saturated fat, 93 mg cholesterol, 253 mg sodium, 2 g dietary fiber

Exchanges: ½ starch, 1 other carbohydrate, ½ very lean meat, 3 fat

Italian Plain Cakes with Strawberries

Cakes

1½	cups whole grain pastry flour
¼	cup + 1½ teaspoons sugar
2	tablespoons chilled butter, cut into small pieces
1	teaspoon baking powder
½	teaspoon baking soda
¼	teaspoon salt
½–⅔	cup low-fat buttermilk
1	tablespoon canola oil
½	teaspoon vanilla extract
2	teaspoons fat-free milk

Filling

1	pint strawberries, cut into ¼" slices
1	tablespoon sugar
1	cup (8 ounces) fat-free vanilla yogurt

To make the cakes: Preheat the oven to 425°F. Coat a baking sheet with cooking spray.

In a large bowl, combine the flour, ¼ cup of the sugar, the butter, baking powder, baking soda, and salt. Mix with your fingers to form crumbs.

In a small bowl, mix ½ cup of the buttermilk, the oil, and vanilla extract. Make a well in the center of the flour mixture and add the buttermilk mixture. With a fork, stir just until combined, adding additional buttermilk as necessary to form a sticky dough. Do not overmix.

Place the dough on a floured surface and sprinkle with a little flour. With your fingertips, gently pat the dough into a 7" circle. With a sharp knife, cut the circle into 8 wedges. Place on the prepared baking sheet, leaving room between the pieces. Brush the milk over the cakes and sprinkle lightly with the remaining 1½ teaspoons sugar.

Bake for 10 to 12 minutes, or until golden. Cool on a rack for 5 minutes.

To make the filling: In a medium bowl, toss the strawberries with the sugar. With the back of a wooden spoon, crush a few of the strawberries. Stir and allow to stand for 5 minutes, or until a light syrup forms.

Split the cakes horizontally with a serrated knife. Spoon the strawberries and yogurt onto the bottom half of each cake. Top with the other half and serve immediately.

Makes 8 servings

Per serving: 177 calories, 5 g protein, 30 g carbohydrates, 5 g fat, 2 g saturated fat, 9 mg cholesterol, 221 mg sodium, 3 g dietary fiber

Exchanges: 1 starch, 1 other carbohydrate, 1 fat

Baking Tip: In Italy, plain cakes with fruit are usually served with coffee or tea and are often enjoyed for breakfast. Each region has a variation on a plain cake, and all are distinguished by their simplicity. These simple cakes resemble our shortcakes. They may be made a day ahead and kept in an airtight container. Add the berries and yogurt just before serving.

Vanilla Cheesecake with Berry Sauce

   3   egg whites

1¼   cups vanilla wafer cookie crumbs

   1   tablespoon butter, melted

   3   tablespoons + 1¼ cups sugar

1½   pounds 1% cottage cheese

   8   ounces reduced-fat cream cheese, at room temperature

   8   ounces fat-free cream cheese, at room temperature

  ¼   cup whole grain pastry flour

   1   egg

   1   tablespoon vanilla extract

   1   pint mixed berries, such as blackberries, raspberries, and blueberries

  ¼   cup strawberry all-fruit syrup

Preheat the oven to 325°F. Coat a 9" springform pan with cooking spray.

Place 1 egg white in a medium bowl. Beat lightly with a fork. Add the cookie crumbs, butter, and 3 tablespoons of the sugar. Toss until the crumbs cling together. Press into the bottom and 2" up the sides of the prepared pan.

In a food processor, combine the cottage cheese, reduced-fat cream cheese, and fat-free cream cheese. Process until smooth. Add the flour and the remaining 1¼ cups sugar. Process until the sugar is dissolved.

Add the egg, vanilla extract, and the remaining 2 egg whites. Process just until blended. Pour over the prepared crust.

Bake for 1 hour and 15 minutes. Turn off the oven and leave the cheesecake in the oven for 30 minutes.

Cool on a rack. Cover and refrigerate for at least 6 hours.

In a medium bowl, mix the berries and syrup. Crush a few of the berries with the back of a wooden spoon. Let stand for 5 minutes, or until a light syrup forms. Serve over slices of the cheesecake.

Makes 12 servings

Per serving: 174 calories, 14 g protein, 15 g carbohydrates, 6 g fat, 4 g saturated fat, 35 mg cholesterol, 435 mg sodium, 1 g dietary fiber

Exchanges: ½ starch, ½ other carbohydrate, ½ lean meat, 1½ very lean meat, 1 fat

Lemon-Orange Cheesecake

1¼   *cups graham cracker crumbs*
 ¼   *cup pecans, toasted and ground*
1¾   *cups sugar*
  3   *tablespoons butter, melted*
  3   *egg whites*
 16   *ounces fat-free cream cheese*
  8   *ounces reduced-fat cream cheese*
 ¼   *cup whole wheat pastry flour*
 ½   *cup lemon juice*
  2   *eggs*
  1   *can (15–16 ounces) mandarin orange sections, drained*
  3   *tablespoons apple jelly*

Preheat the oven to 350°F. Coat a 9" springform pan with cooking spray.

In a large bowl, combine the cracker crumbs, pecans, ¼ cup of the sugar, and butter.

Lightly beat 1 of the egg whites in a cup. Add half of the egg white to the bowl; reserve the remainder for another use or discard. Mix well. Press the mixture into the bottom and 1" up the sides of the prepared pan.

Bake for 10 minutes, or until lightly browned. Cool on a rack.

Meanwhile, place the fat-free cream cheese and reduced-fat cream cheese in a food processor. Process for 1 minute, or until smooth. Add the flour and the 1½ cups remaining sugar. Process for 3 minutes, or until light and fluffy; stop and scrape the sides of the bowl as necessary. Add the lemon juice and process briefly. Add the eggs and the remaining 2 egg whites, one at a time, and process until just incorporated.

Place the mixture in the prepared crust. Bake for 1 hour. Remove from the oven.

Place on a rack and let cool to room temperature. Arrange the drained mandarin orange sections on top of the cake.

In a saucepan over medium heat, warm the jelly and brush with a pastry brush over the orange sections. Cover and refrigerate for at least 8 hours.

Makes 12 servings

Per serving: 326 calories, 11 g protein, 49 g carbohydrates, 10 g fat, 5 g saturated fat, 56 mg cholesterol, 363 mg sodium, 1 g dietary fiber

Exchanges: ½ starch, ½ fruit, 2 other carbohydrate, 1½ fat, ½ meat, 1 very lean meat

Simple Strawberry Cheesecake

Crust

1	cup graham cracker crumbs (see Baking Tip, opposite)
¼	cup milled flaxseeds
¼	cup raw oat bran
1	ounce fat-free cream cheese, warmed in the microwave
⅓	cup water

Filling

2	cups low-fat cottage cheese
1	package (28 grams) powdered Jell-O Sugar Free, Fat Free Instant Pudding, cheesecake flavor
3	ounces fat-free cream cheese

Topping

1	cup sliced strawberries
4	tablespoons sugar-free strawberry jam

To make the crust: Coat a 9" pie pan with cooking spray.

In a large bowl, mix the graham cracker crumbs, flaxseeds, oat bran, cream cheese, and water. Stir the mixture until it's all the same consistency, then press it into the prepared pan, easing the crust up the sides of the pan.

To make the filling: Blend the cottage cheese, pudding mix, and cream cheese in a blender on high until smooth and creamy. Pour the blended mixture into the crust and refrigerate for 1 hour. Top with the strawberries and jam.

Makes 6 servings

Per serving: 199 calories, 14 g protein, 20 g carbohydrates, 5 g fat, 1 g saturated fat, 8 mg cholesterol, 651 mg sodium, 3 g dietary fiber

Exchanges: 1 starch, ½ fat, 1½ very lean meat

Baking Tip: A simple way to crush graham crackers is to place them in a plastic food storage bag, seal the bag, and use a rolling pin to break them into coarse crumbs.

Creamy Chocolate Cheesecake

18	chocolate graham crackers, crushed (see Baking Tip on page 35)
2	tablespoons butter, melted
24	ounces reduced-fat cream cheese, at room temperature
1¼	cups sugar
2	egg whites
1	egg
¾	cup unsweetened cocoa powder
1	tablespoon vanilla extract
½	teaspoon almond extract
¼	teaspoon salt

Preheat the oven to 325°F. Coat a 9" springform pan with cooking spray.

In a small bowl, mix the graham cracker crumbs and butter. Press onto the bottom and 2" up the sides of the prepared pan. Bake for 10 minutes. Cool on a rack.

Place the cream cheese and sugar in a large bowl. Using an electric mixer on medium speed, beat until smooth. Add the egg whites, egg, cocoa powder, vanilla extract, almond extract, and salt. Beat for 5 minutes, or until smooth. Pour into the prepared pan.

Bake for 1 hour and 15 minutes. Turn off the oven and leave the cheesecake in the oven for 1 hour.

Cool on a rack. Cover and refrigerate for at least 2 hours.

Makes 16 servings

Per serving: 280 calories, 7 g protein, 33 g carbohydrates, 11 g fat, 6 g saturated fat, 40 mg cholesterol, 280 mg sodium, 2 g dietary fiber

Exchanges: 1 starch, 1 other starch, 1 lean meat, 2 fat

Pumpkin Cake

1   can (29 ounces) plain pumpkin

1½   cups fat-free milk

¾   cup nonfat dry milk

6   egg whites

¾   cup granulated sugar

1½   teaspoons ground cinnamon

1½   teaspoons ground allspice

1   package (9 ounces) yellow cake mix

⅓   cup packed light brown sugar

4   tablespoons chilled butter, cut into small pieces

¾   cup chopped pecans

Preheat the oven to 350°F. Coat a 13" x 9" baking dish with cooking spray.

In a large bowl, combine the pumpkin, milk, and dry milk. Using an electric mixer on medium speed, beat until smooth. Beat in the egg whites, granulated sugar, cinnamon, and allspice. Pour into the prepared baking dish.

In a medium bowl, combine the cake mix, brown sugar, and butter. Mix with your fingers to form crumbs. Sprinkle over the pumpkin mixture. Top with the pecans.

Cover with foil and bake for 45 minutes. Remove the foil and bake for 15 to 20 minutes, or until a wooden pick inserted in the center comes out clean. Cool on a rack.

Makes 16 servings

Per serving: 235 calories, 7 g protein, 35 g carbohydrates, 9 g fat, 3 g saturated fat, 10 mg cholesterol, 200 mg sodium, 3 g dietary fiber

Exchanges: ½ starch, ½ milk, 1½ other carbohydrate, ½ lean meat, ½ fat

Spice Cake with Maple Glaze

¼   cup canola oil

¼   cup apple butter

¼   cup apple juice

1   teaspoon vanilla extract

1½   cups whole grain pastry flour

1   cup granulated sugar

2   teaspoons baking powder

1   teaspoon ground cinnamon

¼   teaspoon ground cloves

¼   teaspoon ground allspice

¼   teaspoon salt

8   egg whites, at room temperature

4   tablespoons confectioners' sugar

¼   cup maple syrup

Preheat the oven to 350°F. Coat a 10-cup Bundt pan with cooking spray. Dust with flour.

In a small bowl, whisk together the oil, apple butter, apple juice, and vanilla extract.

In a large bowl, mix the flour, granulated sugar, baking powder, cinnamon, cloves, allspice, and salt. Whisk in the apple juice mixture.

Place the egg whites in another large bowl. Using an electric mixer on medium speed, beat until foamy. Add 2 tablespoons of the confectioners' sugar. Increase the speed to high and beat until stiff, glossy peaks form. Fold into the batter until no streaks of white remain. Pour into the prepared pan.

Bake for 20 to 25 minutes, or until a wooden pick inserted in the center comes out clean.

Cool on a rack for 5 minutes. Remove from the pan and place on the rack. Use a wooden skewer to poke holes in the top of the cake.

Place the maple syrup in a small microwaveable bowl. Microwave on high power for 30 seconds, or until warm. Drizzle evenly over the cake and let cool completely. Dust with the remaining 2 tablespoons of the confectioners' sugar.

Makes 12 servings

Per serving: 197 calories, 4 g protein, 36 g carbohydrates, 5 g fat, 0 g saturated fat, 0 mg cholesterol, 170 mg sodium, 2 g dietary fiber

Exchanges: ½ starch, 1½ other carbohydrate, ½ very lean meat, 1 fat

Carrot Cake

Cake

2¾	*cups whole grain pastry flour*
2	*teaspoons baking powder*
2	*teaspoons baking soda*
2	*teaspoons ground cinnamon*
1	*teaspoon ground nutmeg*
¼	*teaspoon salt*
2	*eggs*
4	*egg whites*
1	*cup packed light brown sugar*
1	*cup (8 ounces) fat-free plain or vanilla yogurt*
¼	*cup canola oil*
2	*cups grated carrots*
1	*cup canned crushed pineapple, drained*
⅔	*cup currants*

Frosting

8	*ounces reduced-fat cream cheese, at room temperature*
1	*box (16 ounces) confectioners' sugar*
2	*teaspoons vanilla extract*

To make the cake: Preheat the oven to 325°F. Coat a 13" x 9" baking dish with cooking spray.

In a medium bowl, mix the flour, baking powder, baking soda, cinnamon, nutmeg, and salt.

Place the eggs and egg whites in a large bowl. Using an electric mixer on medium speed, beat until foamy. Add the brown sugar. Beat for 3 minutes. Add the yogurt and oil. Beat until creamy.

On low speed, beat in the flour mixture. Stir in the carrots, pineapple, and currants. Pour into the prepared baking dish.

Bake for 40 to 50 minutes, or until a wooden pick inserted in the center comes out clean. Cool on a rack.

To make the frosting: In a large bowl, combine the cream cheese, confectioners' sugar, and vanilla extract. Using an electric mixer on low speed, beat just until smooth. Spread over the cooled cake.

Makes 16 servings

Per serving: 274 calories, 6 g protein, 49 g carbohydrates, 7 g fat, 2 g saturated fat, 35 mg cholesterol, 330 mg sodium, 2 g dietary fiber

Exchanges: ½ starch, ½ vegetable, 2 other carbohydrate, ½ lean meat, 1 fat

Apple Cake

3   cups whole grain pastry flour
1   cup + 5 tablespoons sugar
3   teaspoons baking powder
1   cup olive oil
¾   cup egg whites
½   cup orange juice
2½ teaspoons vanilla extract
¼   cup chopped walnuts
¼   cup semisweet chocolate chips
4   Granny Smith apples, peeled and sliced
1   tablespoon ground cinnamon

Preheat the oven to 350°F. Coat a 10" tube pan with cooking spray and lightly dust with flour.

In a large bowl, combine the flour, 1 cup of the sugar, and the baking powder.

In a medium bowl, combine the oil, egg whites, orange juice, and vanilla extract. Gradually stir the oil mixture into the flour mixture. Stir in the walnuts and chocolate chips.

Place the apples in another large bowl and top with the remaining 5 tablespoons sugar and the cinnamon. Stir to combine.

Pour a layer of the batter into the prepared pan. Top with a layer of apples. Repeat layering, ending with batter.

Bake for 1 hour and 30 minutes, or until a wooden pick inserted in the center comes out almost clean.

Makes 20 servings

Per serving: 239 calories, 3 g protein, 30 g carbohydrates, 13 g fat, 2 g saturated fat, 0 mg cholesterol, 89 mg sodium, 2 g dietary fiber

Exchanges: ½ starch, 1 other carbohydrate, 2½ fat

Gingerbread Cake with Peach Whipped Cream

Photograph on page 64

1½	cups oat flour
¾	cup whole grain pastry flour
2	teaspoons baking powder
1	teaspoon ground ginger
1	teaspoon ground cinnamon
½	teaspoon ground cloves
	Pinch of salt
⅓	cup canola oil
¼	cup light molasses
1¼	cups hot tap water
1	teaspoon baking soda
1	egg
1	egg yolk
¼	cup sugar
½	cup heavy cream, chilled
3	tablespoons peach all-fruit preserves, melted

Preheat the oven to 350°F. Coat an 8" round cake pan with cooking spray.

In a medium bowl, mix the oat flour, pastry flour, baking powder, ginger, cinnamon, cloves, and salt.

In a large bowl, mix the oil and molasses.

In a 2-cup glass measure, mix the water and baking soda. Whisk into the molasses mixture.

Gradually whisk in the flour mixture. Whisk in the egg, egg yolk, and sugar. Pour into the prepared pan.

Bake for 30 minutes, or until a wooden pick inserted in the center comes out clean. Cool on a rack for 10 minutes. Remove from the pan and place on the rack to cool completely.

Place the cream and preserves in a medium bowl. Using an electric mixer on medium speed, beat until soft peaks form. Serve over wedges of the cake.

Makes 10 servings

Per serving: 248 calories, 4 g protein, 29 g carbohydrates, 13 g fat, 3 g saturated fat, 38 mg cholesterol, 234 mg sodium, 3 g dietary fiber

Exchanges: 1 starch, 1 other carbohydrate, 2½ fat

Spicy Glazed Snacking Cake

Cake

1¾ cups unbleached flour

½ teaspoon baking soda

1 teaspoon baking powder

1 teaspoon ground cinnamon

1 teaspoon ground ginger

¼ teaspoon ground cloves

⅛ teaspoon ground nutmeg

¾ cup low-fat buttermilk

⅔ cup packed brown sugar

¼ cup applesauce

1 egg white

3 tablespoons canola oil

1 teaspoon vanilla extract

Glaze

¾ cup confectioners' sugar

½ teaspoon ground ginger

¼ teaspoon ground cinnamon

1 tablespoon honey

4 teaspoons apple juice or water

½ teaspoon vanilla extract

To make the cake: Preheat the oven to 350°F. Coat an 8" x 8" baking dish with cooking spray.

In a medium bowl, combine the flour, baking soda, baking powder, cinnamon, ginger, cloves, and nutmeg.

In a large bowl, combine the buttermilk, brown sugar, applesauce, egg white, oil, and vanilla extract. Add the flour mixture and stir until just combined.

Spoon the batter into the prepared dish and smooth it evenly. Bake for 30 to 35 minutes, or until a toothpick inserted in the center comes out clean. Cool on a wire rack for 10 to 15 minutes.

To make the glaze: Sift the sugar into a medium bowl. Stir in the ginger and cinnamon. Add the honey, apple juice or water, and vanilla extract. Stir until smooth. Drizzle the glaze over the top of the cooled cake and spread it evenly over the surface.

Makes 8 servings

Per serving: 288 calories, 4 g protein, 55 g carbohydrates, 6 g fat, 1 g saturated fat, 1 mg cholesterol, 179 mg sodium, 1 g dietary fiber

Exchanges: 1½ starch, 1½ other carbohydrate, 1 fat

Cranberry Coffee Cake

Topping

Photograph on page 67

¾	cup packed light brown sugar
½	cup whole grain pastry flour
¼	cup chopped toasted walnuts
2	teaspoons ground cinnamon
2	tablespoons butter, at room temperature

Cake

2	cups whole grain pastry flour
1	teaspoon baking powder
1	teaspoon baking soda
½	teaspoon salt
¼	cup canola oil
1	cup sugar
1	egg
1	egg white
1	tablespoon grated orange rind
1	teaspoon vanilla extract
1	cup reduced-fat sour cream
2	cups cranberries, coarsely chopped

To make the topping: In a small bowl, combine the brown sugar, flour, walnuts, cinnamon, and butter. Mix with your fingers to form crumbs.

To make the cake: Preheat the oven to 350°F. Coat a 13" x 9" baking dish with cooking spray.

In a medium bowl, mix the flour, baking powder, baking soda, and salt.

In a large bowl, combine the oil, sugar, egg, and egg white. Using an electric mixer on medium speed, beat for 3 minutes, or until light in color. Beat in the orange rind and vanilla extract.

On low speed, beat in one-third of the flour mixture and one-half of the sour cream. Repeat, beginning and ending with the flour. Beat for about 2 minutes, or until smooth and thick.

Pour into the prepared baking dish. Scatter the cranberries on top. Sprinkle with the topping.

Bake for 40 to 45 minutes, or until a wooden pick inserted in the center comes out clean. Cool on a rack.

Makes 12 servings

Per serving: 298 calories, 5 g protein, 48 g carbohydrates, 11 g fat, 3 g saturated fat, 30 mg cholesterol, 290 mg sodium, 3 g dietary fiber

Exchanges: 1 starch, 2 other carbohydrate, 2 fat

Baking Tip: **Enjoy this cake in the summer by replacing the cranberries with fresh blueberries.**

Lemon Coffee Cake

2½   *cups whole grain pastry flour*

2½   *teaspoons baking powder*

½   *teaspoon salt*

⅔   *cup honey*

⅓   *cup canola oil*

1   *cup liquid egg substitute*

1½   *teaspoons lemon extract*

1   *cup (8 ounces) fat-free lemon yogurt*

1   *cup coarsely chopped dried cherries or blueberries*

1   *tablespoon grated lemon rind*

Preheat the oven to 325°F. Coat a 10-cup Bundt pan with cooking spray.

In a small bowl, mix the flour, baking powder, and salt.

Place the honey and oil in a large bowl. Using an electric mixer on medium speed, beat until creamy. Beat in the egg substitute and lemon extract.

On low speed, beat in one-third of the flour mixture and one-half of the yogurt. Repeat, beginning and ending with the flour. Beat for 2 minutes, or until smooth and thick. Fold in the cherries or blueberries and lemon rind. Pour into the prepared pan.

Bake for 30 to 35 minutes, or until a wooden pick inserted in the center comes out clean. Cool on a rack for 10 minutes. Remove from the pan and place on the rack to cool completely.

Makes 12 servings

Per serving: 245 calories, 6 g protein, 41 g carbohydrates, 7 g fat, 1 g saturated fat, 0 mg cholesterol, 250 mg sodium, 2 g dietary fiber

Exchanges: 1 starch, ½ fruit, 1 other carbohydrate, ½ lean meat, 1 fat

Orange-Blueberry Loaf

Photograph on page 61

1 cup blueberries

2 tablespoons + 1¾ cups whole grain pastry flour

¼ cup cornmeal

1½ teaspoons baking powder

½ teaspoon baking soda

½ teaspoon salt

¾ cup sugar

6 tablespoons butter, at room temperature

1 egg

½ cup orange juice

2 teaspoons grated orange rind

Preheat the oven to 350°F. Coat an 8" x 4" loaf pan with cooking spray.

In a small bowl, mix the blueberries and 2 tablespoons of the flour.

In a medium bowl, mix the remaining 1¾ cups flour, the cornmeal, baking powder, baking soda, and salt.

Place the sugar and butter in a large bowl. Using an electric mixer on high speed, beat for 3 minutes, or until light and fluffy. Add the egg and beat well. Beat in the orange juice and orange rind.

Add the flour mixture and beat on low speed until well blended. Stir in the blueberries. Pour into the prepared pan.

Bake for 55 to 65 minutes, or until a wooden pick inserted in the center comes out clean. Cool on a rack for 5 minutes. Remove from the pan and place on the rack to cool completely.

Makes 12 servings

Per serving: 174 calories, 3 g protein, 28 g carbohydrates, 6 g fat, 4 g saturated fat, 35 mg cholesterol, 260 mg sodium, 2 g dietary fiber

Exchanges: 1 starch, 1 other carbohydrate, 1 fat

Banana-Nut Bread

½   cup butter, softened

1   cup sugar

1   teaspoon vanilla extract

6   egg whites

3   cups unbleached flour

1½   teaspoons baking powder

½   teaspoon salt

½   cup fat-free milk

2   cups mashed bananas

½   teaspoon grated lemon rind

¾   cup sunflower seeds

Preheat the oven to 400°F. Coat two 8" x 4" loaf pans with cooking spray.

In a large bowl, using an electric mixer on medium speed, beat together the butter, sugar, and vanilla extract on medium speed until light and fluffy. Slowly add the egg whites and beat well.

In a medium bowl, mix the flour, baking powder, and salt with a wire whisk until combined.

Alternately add the flour mixture and milk to the egg mixture, starting and ending with the flour. Mix the batter until it is just smooth. Be careful not to overmix.

Use a spatula to gently fold in the bananas, lemon rind, and sunflower seeds.

Place the batter in the prepared pans, smoothing the top with a rubber spatula.

Bake for 50 to 60 minutes, or until the tops are golden brown and a wooden pick inserted in the center comes out clean. (If the bread browns too quickly as it bakes, place a sheet of foil lightly over the top.) Remove from the oven and cool on a wire rack for 10 to 15 minutes before removing from the pans.

Makes 20 servings

Per serving: 206 calories, 5 g protein, 31 g carbohydrates, 8 g fat, 3 g saturated fat, 12 mg cholesterol, 148 mg sodium, 2 g dietary fiber

Exchanges: 1 starch, ½ fruit, ½ other carbohydrate, 1½ fat, ½ lean meat

Chocolate Spice Bread

1¾ cups unbleached flour
1½ teaspoons baking powder
1 teaspoon baking soda
1 teaspoon ground cinnamon
½ teaspoon ground ginger
½ teaspoon ground anise seeds
¼ teaspoon curry powder
  Pinch of salt
⅔ cup honey
⅔ cup cocoa powder
½ cup + 2 tablespoons orange juice
2 eggs, lightly beaten

Preheat the oven to 325°F. Coat an 8" x 4" loaf pan with cooking spray.

In a medium bowl, sift the flour, baking powder, baking soda, cinnamon, ginger, anise seeds, curry powder, and salt.

In a large saucepan, combine the honey, cocoa powder, and orange juice. Stir over low heat until well mixed. Set aside to cool.

Mix the eggs into the chocolate mixture. Gradually incorporate the flour mixture into the chocolate mixture and mix well.

Pour the batter into the prepared pan and bake for 50 to 60 minutes, or until a wooden pick inserted in the center comes out clean.

Unmold the bread onto a wire rack and allow to cool.

Makes 16 servings

Per serving: 115 calories, 3 g protein, 25 g carbohydrates, 1 g fat, 1 g saturated fat, 26 mg cholesterol, 145 mg sodium, 2 g dietary fiber

Exchanges: ½ starch, ½ other carbohydrate

Orange and Poppy Seed Cake

Cake

2	cups whole grain pastry flour
½	cup poppy seeds
½	teaspoon baking powder
½	teaspoon salt
4	egg whites, at room temperature
2	eggs, at room temperature
1¼	cups sugar
¼	cup canola oil
2	tablespoons grated orange rind
1	teaspoon vanilla extract
¾	cup orange juice

Glaze

½	cup confectioners' sugar
1–2	tablespoons orange juice

To make the cake: Preheat the oven to 350°F. Coat a 10" tube pan with a removable bottom with cooking spray. Dust with flour.

In a medium bowl, mix the flour, poppy seeds, baking powder, and salt.

Place the egg whites in a large bowl. Using an electric mixer on medium speed, beat until soft peaks form.

In another large bowl, beat the whole eggs and sugar on medium speed until pale yellow and fluffy. Beat in the oil, orange rind, and vanilla extract. On low speed, beat in one-third of the flour mixture and one-half of the orange juice. Repeat, beginning and ending with the flour.

Gently stir one-third of the egg whites into the batter. Fold in the remaining whites until no streaks of white remain. Pour into the prepared pan.

Bake for 40 minutes, or until a wooden pick inserted in the center comes out clean. Run a knife around the rim of the cake to loosen it from the sides. Cool on a rack for 15 minutes. Remove from the pan and place on the rack to cool completely.

To make the glaze: In a small bowl, whisk together the sugar and orange juice until smooth. Drizzle over the cooled cake.

Makes 12 servings

Per serving: 242 calories, 5 g protein, 39 g carbohydrates, 8 g fat, 1 g saturated fat, 35 mg cholesterol, 144 mg sodium, 2 g dietary fiber

Exchanges: 1 starch, ½ vegetable, 1½ other carbohydrate, ½ lean meat, 1½ fat

Baking Tip: Adding the glaze to this cake makes a lovely presentation, but it does add some extra sugar. Save this presentation for special occasions. Serve the cake unglazed for everyday events.

Coconut Cream Bundt Cake

2   *cups whole grain pastry flour*

2   *teaspoons baking powder*

½   *teaspoon baking soda*

½   *teaspoon salt*

4   *egg whites, at room temperature*

½   *teaspoon cream of tartar*

1¼   *cups light coconut milk*

1   *cup sugar*

4   *egg yolks, at room temperature*

2   *teaspoons vanilla extract*

⅔   *cup sweetened shredded coconut*

Preheat the oven to 350°F. Coat a 10-cup Bundt pan with cooking spray.

In a medium bowl, mix the flour, baking powder, baking soda, and salt.

Place the egg whites in a large bowl. Using an electric mixer on medium speed, beat until frothy. Add the cream of tartar and beat until stiff peaks form.

In another medium bowl, beat the coconut milk, sugar, egg yolks, and vanilla extract on medium speed for 3 minutes. With the mixer on low speed, gradually add the flour mixture. Fold in the egg whites and coconut. Pour into the prepared cake pan.

Bake for 35 minutes, or until a wooden pick inserted in the center comes out clean. Cool on a rack for 10 minutes. Remove from the pan and place on the rack to cool completely.

Makes 12 servings

Per serving: 161 calories, 4 g protein, 29 g carbohydrates, 4 g fat, 2 g saturated fat, 70 mg cholesterol, 250 mg sodium, 2 g dietary fiber

Exchanges: 1 starch, 1 other carbohydrate, ½ lean meat, 1 fat

Baking Tip: Coconut milk is a thick, creamy white infusion of coconut meat and water. Unlike cream of coconut, coconut milk is unsweetened and most often used in Indian and Southeast Asian curries. Look for it in the ethnic section of your supermarket.

Sour Cream Muffins

2 cups whole grain pastry flour

½ cup sugar

2½ teaspoons baking powder

½ teaspoon baking soda

½ teaspoon salt

1 cup dried cranberries or raisins

¾ cup fat-free milk

½ cup reduced-fat sour cream

3 tablespoons canola oil

1 egg

1 teaspoon vanilla extract

Preheat the oven to 400°F. Coat a 12-cup muffin pan with cooking spray.

In a medium bowl, mix the flour, sugar, baking powder, baking soda, and salt. Stir in the cranberries or raisins.

In a large bowl, mix the milk, sour cream, oil, egg, and vanilla extract. Stir in the flour mixture just until combined. Divide the batter evenly among the prepared muffin cups.

Bake for 12 to 15 minutes, or until a wooden pick inserted in the center of a muffin comes out clean. Cool on a rack for 5 minutes. Remove from the pan and place on the rack to cool completely.

Makes 12

Per muffin: 172 calories, 4 g protein, 28 g carbohydrates, 5 g fat, 1 g saturated fat, 25 mg cholesterol, 250 mg sodium, 2 g dietary fiber

Exchanges: 1 starch, ½ fruit, ½ other carbohydrate, 1 fat

Light Lemon Cupcakes

Cupcakes

1   *cup unbleached flour*

½   *cup sugar*

¼   *cup instant nonfat dry milk*

1   *teaspoon baking powder*

¼   *teaspoon baking soda*

¼   *teaspoon salt*

5   *tablespoons softened butter*

½   *cup (4 ounces) fat-free lemon-flavored yogurt*

1   *egg*

¼   *cup water*

¼   *teaspoon lemon extract*

Icing

1   *cup confectioners' sugar*

2   *teaspoons lemon juice*

1   *tablespoon water*

To make the cupcakes: Preheat the oven to 350°F. Line a 12-cup muffin pan with paper liners.

In a large bowl, combine the flour, sugar, dry milk, baking powder, baking soda, salt, butter, and yogurt. Using an electric mixer on medium speed, beat until the butter is thoroughly incorporated into the dry ingredients.

In a cup, mix the egg with the water and lemon extract. Add to the flour mixture and beat until smooth.

Spoon the batter into the paper-lined cups. Bake for 25 minutes, or until the cupcakes are lightly browned and spring back when lightly touched in the center. Remove from the pans and cool completely on wire racks.

To make the icing: In a 2-cup measuring cup or small bowl, mix together the sugar, lemon juice, and water. Evenly drizzle over the cupcakes.

Makes 12

Per cupcake: 180 calories, 3 g protein, 29 g carbohydrates, 6 g fat, 4 g saturated fat, 33 mg cholesterol, 172 mg sodium, 3 g dietary fiber

Exchanges: ½ starch, 1 other carbohydrate, 1 fat

Variation

Pineapple Upside-Down Cupcakes: *Coat the 12-cup muffin pan with cooking spray; omit the paper liners. Spoon 2 teaspoons Splenda Brown Sugar Blend into each cup. Top with ½ teaspoon unsalted butter and ¼ of one ring of pineapple. Spoon the cupcake batter into the cups on top of the pineapple. Bake as directed. Invert onto a serving tray while the cupcakes are hot. Omit the icing.*

Per cupcake: 200 calories, 3 g protein, 30 g carbohydrates, 8 g fat, 5 g saturated fat, 38 mg cholesterol, 174 mg sodium, 4 g dietary fiber

Exchanges: ½ starch, ½ other carbohydrate, 1½ fat

Cobblers *and* Crisps

Cobblers and crisps have been called by various names, such as grunts, slumps, buckles, crunches, betties, crumbles, and many others. Whatever you call them, these deep-dish favorites rely on great taste more than long prep times and fancy crusts. Their main ingredient, fruit, makes the perfect start to any dessert because it is already naturally high in fiber. These recipes have been made even better for you with the addition of healthier toppings. Cutting back butter where possible, as well as using old-fashioned oats and whole grain pastry flour, keeps the warm, crunchy texture and helps reduce fat and calories.

Pear and Almond Crisp

4	large pears, cored and cut into $\frac{1}{2}$" slices
2	tablespoons maple syrup
1	tablespoon lemon juice
1	teaspoon vanilla extract
$\frac{1}{2}$	teaspoon ground nutmeg
1	cup old-fashioned rolled oats
$\frac{1}{3}$	cup sliced almonds
$\frac{1}{4}$	cup packed light brown sugar
2	tablespoons whole grain pastry flour
2	tablespoons chilled butter, cut into small pieces
2	tablespoons canola oil

Preheat the oven to 350°F. Coat an 11" x 7" baking dish with cooking spray.

In a large bowl, mix the pears, maple syrup, lemon juice, vanilla, and nutmeg. Place in the prepared baking dish.

In a medium bowl, combine the oats, almonds, brown sugar, flour, butter, and oil. Mix with your fingers to form crumbs. Sprinkle over the pear mixture.

Bake for 40 minutes, or until the pears are tender and the topping is lightly browned. Cool on a rack for at least 10 minutes before serving.

Makes 8 servings

Per serving: 225 calories, 4 g protein, 32 g carbohydrates, 10 g fat, 2 g saturated fat, 10 mg cholesterol, 35 mg sodium, 4 g dietary fiber

Exchanges: $\frac{1}{2}$ starch, 1 fruit, $\frac{1}{2}$ other carbohydrate, 2 fat

Orange-Blueberry Loaf   *page 49*

Strawberry Cream Cake *page 26*

Gingerbread Cake with Peach Whipped Cream   *page 43*

Tiramisu   *page 250*

Cranberry Coffee Cake *page 46*

Strawberry Shortcakes
page 264

Chocolate-Raspberry Cake   *page 20*

Key Lime Pie   *page 106*

Peach Clafouti *page 260*

Strawberry-Rhubarb Cobbler *page 82*

Apple and Cranberry Crisp   *page 80*

Apple Crumble with Toasted-Oat Topping   *page 91*

Pear and Cranberry Crisp *page 79*

Plum and Blueberry Cobbler   *page 87*

Banana Split Shake   *page 214*

Peanut Butter Ice Cream Shake
page 212

Peach and Blueberry Crisp

2 *pounds peaches, peeled, pitted, and cut into ½" slices*

2 *cups blueberries*

⅓ *cup apricot nectar or peach nectar*

¼ *cup granulated sugar*

2 *tablespoons + ½ cup whole grain pastry flour*

1 *tablespoon lemon juice*

¼ *cup old-fashioned rolled oats*

¼ *cup packed light brown sugar*

3 *tablespoons chilled butter, cut into small pieces*

½ *teaspoon ground cinnamon*

Preheat the oven to 375°F. Coat a 9" x 9" baking dish with cooking spray.

In a large bowl, mix the peaches, blueberries, nectar, granulated sugar, 2 tablespoons of the flour, and the lemon juice. Place in the prepared baking dish.

In a medium bowl, combine the oats, brown sugar, butter, cinnamon, and the remaining ½ cup flour. Mix with your fingers to form crumbs. Sprinkle over the peach mixture.

Bake for 45 to 50 minutes, or until the top is lightly browned. Cool on a rack for 10 minutes before serving.

Makes 8 servings

Per serving: 168 calories, 3 g protein, 33 g carbohydrates, 5 g fat, 3 g saturated fat, 10 mg cholesterol, 45 mg sodium, 4 g dietary fiber

Exchanges: ½ starch, 1 fruit, ½ other carbohydrate, 1 fat

Baking Tip: To peel peaches, drop them into boiling water for about 20 seconds. Remove with a slotted spoon and run under cold water. Use a paring knife to score the peel and remove it.

South Pacific Crisp

1   pineapple, peeled, cored, and cut into 1" cubes,
    or 1 can (16 ounces) pineapple tidbits in juice, drained

6   peaches, peeled, pitted, and cut into 1" cubes

¾   cup orange juice

1   teaspoon rum extract

1   tablespoon cornstarch

¼   cup + ⅓ cup packed light brown sugar

1¼ cups coarsely chopped low-fat gingersnaps

1   cup old-fashioned rolled oats

¼   cup sweetened shredded coconut

2   tablespoons chilled butter, cut into small pieces

½   teaspoon ground cinnamon

Preheat the oven to 375°F. Lightly coat a 9" x 9" baking dish with cooking spray.

In a large bowl, combine the pineapple, peaches, orange juice, rum extract, cornstarch, and ¼ cup of the brown sugar. Stir until the brown sugar and cornstarch are dissolved. Place in the prepared baking dish.

In a medium bowl, combine the gingersnaps, oats, coconut, butter, cinnamon, and the remaining ⅓ cup brown sugar. Mix with your fingers to form coarse crumbs. Sprinkle over the pineapple mixture.

Bake for 35 to 40 minutes, or until golden brown and bubbling. Cool on a rack for 15 minutes before serving.

Makes 12 servings

Per serving: 112 calories, 2 g protein, 20 g carbohydrates, 3 g fat, 2 g saturated fat, 5 mg cholesterol, 40 mg sodium, 2 g dietary fiber

Exchanges: ½ starch, 1 fruit, ½ fat

Pear and Cranberry Crisp

Photograph on page 74

1   lemon

8   ripe pears, cored and cut into ½" chunks

1   cup dried cranberries

⅔   cup pear nectar or apple juice

⅓   cup granulated sugar

3   tablespoons + ¼ cup whole grain pastry flour

⅔   cup old-fashioned rolled oats

¼   cup packed light brown sugar

2   tablespoons butter, melted

1   teaspoon ground cinnamon

HEALTH BONUS:
One serving of this crisp supplies 7 grams of fiber, which can be a tremendous benefit to people with diabetes. Fiber slows the absorption of fats and carbohydrates into the system, reducing their adverse effects on the glucose-insulin system. In one small study, 13 people who ate 50 grams of fiber each day achieved a 10 percent drop in their blood sugar levels. And because high-fiber foods are filling, you tend to eat less of them.

Preheat the oven to 375°F. Coat a 1½-quart baking dish with cooking spray.

Grate 1 teaspoon of rind from the lemon into a large bowl. Cut the lemon in half and squeeze the juice into the bowl. Add the pears, cranberries, pear nectar or apple juice, granulated sugar, and 3 tablespoons of the flour. Toss to mix. Place in the prepared baking dish.

In a medium bowl, mix the oats, brown sugar, butter, cinnamon, and the remaining ¼ cup flour. Sprinkle over the pear mixture.

Bake for 40 to 50 minutes, or until the filling is bubbling and the top is browned. Cool on a rack for at least 10 minutes before serving.

Makes 8 servings

Per serving: 262 calories, 3 g protein, 57 g carbohydrates, 4 g fat, 2 g saturated fat, 10 mg cholesterol, 35 mg sodium, 7 g dietary fiber

Exchanges: ½ starch, 3 fruit, ½ other carbohydrate, ½ fat

Apple and Cranberry Crisp

Photograph on page 72

3 large Empire, Jonagold, Gala, or Granny Smith apples, cored and sliced into ¼" wedges

½ cup dried cranberries

3 tablespoons frozen apple juice concentrate, thawed

1 tablespoon granulated sugar

¾ cup old-fashioned rolled oats

⅓ cup whole grain pastry flour

¼ cup packed dark brown sugar

3 tablespoons chilled butter, cut into small pieces

⅛ teaspoon salt

⅛ teaspoon ground allspice

Preheat the oven to 425°F. Coat a 9" x 9" baking dish with cooking spray.

In a large bowl, mix the apples, cranberries, apple juice concentrate, and granulated sugar. Place in the prepared baking dish.

In a medium bowl, combine the oats, flour, brown sugar, butter, salt, and allspice. Mix with your fingers to form crumbs. Sprinkle over the apple mixture.

Cover with foil and bake for 20 minutes, or until the mixture is bubbly and the apples are tender. Uncover and bake for 5 to 10 minutes, or until the topping is lightly browned. Cool on a rack for at least 10 minutes before serving.

Makes 8 servings

Per serving: 171 calories, 2 g protein, 31 g carbohydrates, 5 g fat, 3 g saturated fat, 10 mg cholesterol, 95 mg sodium, 4 g dietary fiber

Exchanges: ½ starch, 1 fruit, ½ other carbohydrate, 1 fat

Baking Tip: Dried fruits add a nice sweetness to baked goods while also offering the nutritional benefits of vitamins, minerals, and fiber. Besides the classic dried fruits such as prunes, figs, and apricots, look for dried cherries, blueberries, and strawberries to liven up dishes. They are all interchangeable in recipes. Use whatever you have on hand at the time.

Pineapple Crumble

1   *pineapple, peeled, cored, and cut into ½" chunks*

3   *tablespoons honey*

1½   *teaspoons vanilla extract*

½   *teaspoon ground cardamom*

1   *cup whole grain pastry flour*

¼   *cup wheat germ*

3   *tablespoons chilled butter, cut into small pieces*

2   *tablespoons packed dark brown sugar*

2   *tablespoons sweetened shredded coconut*

¼   *teaspoon salt*

Preheat the oven to 425°F. Coat an 11" x 7" baking dish with cooking spray.

In a large bowl, mix the pineapple, honey, vanilla extract, and ¼ teaspoon of the cardamom. Place in the prepared baking dish.

In a medium bowl, combine the flour, wheat germ, butter, brown sugar, coconut, salt, and the remaining ¼ teaspoon cardamom. Mix with your fingers to form coarse crumbs. Sprinkle over the pineapple mixture.

Bake for 25 to 30 minutes, or until the topping is browned and the fruit is bubbling. Cool on a rack for at least 10 minutes before serving.

Makes 8 servings

Per serving: 189 calories, 3 g protein, 35 g carbohydrates, 6 g fat, 3 g saturated fat, 10 mg cholesterol, 125 mg sodium, 3 g dietary fiber

Exchanges: ½ starch, 1 fruit, ½ other carbohydrate, 1 fat

Strawberry-Rhubarb Cobbler

Photograph on page 71

Filling

1	quart strawberries, halved or quartered if large
3	cups sliced rhubarb
½	cup sugar
¼	cup water
1	tablespoon cornstarch
2	tablespoons raspberry liqueur or orange juice

Top Crust

1	cup whole grain pastry flour
1	teaspoon baking powder
½	teaspoon baking soda
⅛	teaspoon salt
4	teaspoons sugar
2	tablespoons chilled butter, cut into small pieces
1	tablespoon fat-free plain yogurt
1–2	tablespoons fat-free milk
¼	teaspoon ground cinnamon

Preheat the oven to 400°F. Coat a 3-quart baking dish with cooking spray.

To make the filling: Place half of the strawberries in a large saucepan. Add the rhubarb, sugar, and water. Cover and cook over medium heat, stirring occasionally, for 10 minutes.

Place the cornstarch in a cup. Add the liqueur or orange juice and stir until smooth. Add to the saucepan and cook, stirring constantly, for 1 minute, or until thickened. Stir in the remaining strawberries. Pour the mixture into the prepared baking dish.

To make the top crust: In a medium bowl, mix the flour, baking powder, baking soda, salt, and 2 teaspoons of the sugar. Cut in the butter and yogurt until the mixture resembles coarse crumbs. Add the milk, 1 tablespoon at a time, and stir until the dough just holds together.

Turn out onto a lightly floured surface and shape the dough 1" smaller than the size of the baking dish. Carefully lay the dough over the center of the strawberry mixture.

In a cup, mix the cinnamon and the remaining 2 teaspoons sugar. Sprinkle over the dough.

Bake for 20 to 25 minutes, or until bubbling and golden brown. Cool on a rack for at least 10 minutes before serving.

Makes 12 servings

Per serving: 108 calories, 2 g protein, 22 g carbohydrates, 2 g fat, 1 g saturated fat, 5 mg cholesterol, 190 mg sodium, 3 g dietary fiber

Exchanges: ½ starch, ½ fruit, ½ other carbohydrate, ½ fat

Baking Tip: Another delicious cobbler combination is sweet peaches and Bing cherries. Use 4 cups peeled and sliced peaches and 2 cups pitted and halved Bing cherries. Replace the raspberry liqueur or orange juice with lemon juice.

Blueberry and Almond Cobbler

Blueberries

4	cups fresh or frozen blueberries
½	cup sugar
2	tablespoons cornstarch
1	tablespoon lemon juice
½	teaspoon cinnamon

Topping

1	cup unbleached flour
1½	tablespoons sugar
¼	teaspoon salt
1	teaspoon baking soda
½	teaspoon baking powder
2	tablespoons nondiet tub-style margarine or butter, softened
¾	cup low-fat buttermilk
⅓	cup sliced almonds
½	teaspoon vanilla extract

To make the blueberries: Coat a 9" pie pan with cooking spray.

In a medium saucepan, combine the blueberries, sugar, cornstarch, lemon juice, and cinnamon. Bring to a boil over high heat. Reduce the heat to low. Cook and stir for 2 to 3 minutes, or until the mixture begins to thicken. Pour into the prepared pie pan.

To make the topping: Preheat the oven to 350°F.

In a medium bowl, mix the flour, sugar, salt, baking soda, and baking powder. Using a pastry blender or table knives, cut in the margarine or butter until the mixture resembles coarse crumbs. Add the buttermilk, almonds, and vanilla extract. Mix just until moistened.

Spoon heaping tablespoons of the batter evenly over the blueberries.

Bake for 20 to 25 minutes, or until the blueberries are bubbly and the topping is golden brown.

Makes 6 servings

Per serving: 298 calories, 5 g protein, 56 g carbohydrates, 7 g fat, 1 g saturated fat, 1 mg cholesterol, 432 mg sodium, 4 g dietary fiber

Exchanges: 1 starch, 1 fruit, 1 other carbohydrate, 1 fat

Variations

Cherry Almond Cobbler: *Replace the blueberries with 2 cups pitted sweet cherries and 2 cups pitted sour cherries. Increase the sugar to ⅔ cup.*

Per serving: 319 calories, 5 g protein, 61 g carbohydrates, 7 g fat, 1 g saturated fat, 1 mg cholesterol, 433 mg sodium, 3 g dietary fiber

Exchanges: 1 starch, 1 fruit, 1½ other carbohydrate, 1 fat

Peach Almond Cobbler: *Replace the blueberries with 4 cups fresh or frozen sliced peaches. Increase the sugar to ⅔ cup.*

Per serving: 307 calories, 5 g protein, 58 g carbohydrates, 7 g fat, 1 g saturated fat, 1 mg cholesterol, 431 mg sodium, 3 g dietary fiber

Exchanges: 1 starch, ½ fruit, 1½ other carbohydrate, 1 fat

Peach and Cherry Cobbler

5   large peaches, peeled and pitted

3   cups cherries, pitted and halved

½   cup + 1 teaspoon granulated sugar

1   cup unbleached flour

2   tablespoons dark brown sugar

1   teaspoon baking powder

¼   teaspoon ground nutmeg

6   tablespoons chilled butter or margarine

⅓   cup fat-free sour cream

Preheat the oven to 375°F.

Cut each peach into 8 wedges, then cut each wedge in half crosswise. Place in a shallow 3-quart nonstick baking dish. Sprinkle with the cherries and ½ cup of the granulated sugar; toss to coat the fruit with the sugar.

In the bowl of a food processor, mix the flour, brown sugar, baking powder, and nutmeg. Cut the butter or margarine into 6 pieces and distribute the pieces on top of the flour mixture. Process with on/off turns until the butter or margarine is in pea-size pieces.

Add the sour cream and process with on/off turns until the dough is soft and crumbly. Remove the dough from the food processor and press it together with your hands. Place it on a lightly floured surface.

Roll the dough out to fit the top of your baking dish. Carefully lift and place it over the fruit. Tuck in any edges that stick out; the dough doesn't have to lie smooth.

Brush the top lightly with water and sprinkle on the remaining 1 teaspoon granulated sugar. Make four slashes in the dough to allow steam to escape. Bake for 50 minutes, or until the top is firm and lightly browned and the fruit is bubbling around the edges.

Makes 6 servings

Per serving: 358 calories, 5 g protein, 63 g carbohydrates, 12 g fat, 7 g saturated fat, 31 mg cholesterol, 182 mg sodium, 4 g dietary fiber

Exchanges: 1 starch, 1½ fruit, 1 other carbohydrate, 2 fat

Plum and Blueberry Cobbler

Photograph on page 75

8	plums, pitted and quartered
2	cups blueberries
½	cup + 4 teaspoons sugar
2	tablespoons + 1 cup whole grain pastry flour
¾	teaspoon baking powder
⅛	teaspoon salt
½	cup low-fat buttermilk
1	egg white
1½	tablespoons canola oil

Preheat the oven to 375°F. Coat a 9" x 9" baking dish with cooking spray.

In a large bowl, mix the plums, blueberries, ½ cup of the sugar, and 2 tablespoons of the flour. Place in the prepared baking dish.

In a medium bowl, mix 3 teaspoons of the remaining sugar, the baking powder, salt, and the remaining 1 cup flour.

In a small bowl, mix the buttermilk, egg white, and oil. Pour into the flour mixture. Stir until a thick batter forms. Drop tablespoons of the batter on top of the fruit. Sprinkle with the remaining 1 teaspoon sugar.

Bake for 35 to 40 minutes, or until golden and bubbly. Cool on a rack for at least 10 minutes before serving.

Makes 9 servings

Per serving: 166 calories, 3 g protein, 34 g carbohydrates, 3 g fat, 0 g saturated fat, 0 mg cholesterol, 95 mg sodium, 3 g dietary fiber

Exchanges: ½ starch, 1 fruit, ½ other carbohydrate, ½ fat

Blueberry-Raspberry Bake

⅓   cup raspberry all-fruit preserves

1   tablespoon + 1 teaspoon granulated sugar

1   tablespoon cornstarch

1½   teaspoons grated lemon rind

2   teaspoons lemon juice

2   cups blueberries

2   cups raspberries

1   cup whole grain pastry flour

3   tablespoons packed light brown sugar

1   teaspoon baking powder

¼   teaspoon baking soda

⅛   teaspoon salt

3   tablespoons chilled butter, cut into small pieces

¼   cup low-fat buttermilk or fat-free plain yogurt

Preheat the oven to 425°F. Coat a 9" x 9" baking dish with cooking spray.

In a large bowl, mix the preserves, 1 tablespoon of the granulated sugar, the cornstarch, lemon rind, and lemon juice. Stir in the blueberries and raspberries. Place in the prepared baking dish.

Cover with foil and bake for 20 minutes, or until the fruit is hot and bubbling. Remove from the oven.

In a food processor, combine the flour, brown sugar, baking powder, baking soda, and salt. Pulse to mix. Add the butter and pulse until very fine crumbs form. Add the buttermilk or yogurt and pulse just until a soft dough forms.

On a lightly floured surface, knead the dough 5 times. With a lightly floured rolling pin, roll out the dough to a 7" x 7" square. Place over the hot fruit and sprinkle with the remaining 1 teaspoon granulated sugar.

Bake for 20 to 30 minutes, or until the dough is lightly browned and the fruit is bubbling. Cool on a rack for at least 15 minutes before serving.

Makes 8 servings

Per serving: 159 calories, 2 g protein, 29 g carbohydrates, 5 g fat, 3 g saturated fat, 10 mg cholesterol, 190 mg sodium, 3 g dietary fiber

Exchanges: ½ starch, 1 fruit, ½ other carbohydrate, 1 fat

Peach Crunch

½   cup (4 ounces) fat-free plain yogurt

3   teaspoons apple pie spice

½   cup Grape-Nuts cereal

2   teaspoons honey

1   teaspoon butter

1   package (16 ounces) frozen unsweetened peach slices, thawed, or 3½ cups peeled, pitted, and sliced peaches

In a small bowl, mix the yogurt and 1½ teaspoons of the apple pie spice.

In another small bowl, mix the cereal, honey, and the remaining 1½ teaspoons apple pie spice.

Coat a small nonstick skillet with cooking spray. Add the butter and place over medium heat until melted. Add the cereal mixture. Cook and stir for 2 minutes, or until the butter is absorbed.

Spoon the peaches into 4 dessert bowls. Top with the yogurt mixture and sprinkle with the cereal mixture.

Makes 4 servings

Per serving: 152 calories, 4 g protein, 34 g carbohydrates, 1 g fat, 1 g saturated fat, 5 mg cholesterol, 120 mg sodium, 4 g dietary fiber

Exchanges: ½ starch, 1 fruit, ½ other carbohydrate

Apple Crumble with Toasted-Oat Topping

*Photograph
on page 73*

6   *medium Jonagold or Golden Delicious apples,
cored and thinly sliced*

½   *cup unsweetened applesauce*

¾   *cup old-fashioned rolled oats*

3   *tablespoons wheat germ*

3   *tablespoons packed light brown sugar*

1   *tablespoon canola oil*

1   *tablespoon chilled butter, cut into small pieces*

1   *teaspoon ground cinnamon*

Preheat the oven to 350°F. Coat a 13" x 9" baking dish with cooking spray.

In a large bowl, mix the apples and applesauce. Place in the prepared baking dish.

In a small bowl, combine the oats, wheat germ, brown sugar, oil, butter, and cinnamon.
Mix with your fingers to form crumbs. Sprinkle over the apples.

Bake for 30 minutes, or until the topping is golden and the apples are bubbling. Cool on
a rack for at least 10 minutes before serving.

Makes 6 servings

Per serving: 181 calories, 3 g protein, 33 g carbohydrates, 6 g fat, 2 g saturated fat, 5 mg cholesterol, 7 mg
sodium, 3 g dietary fiber

Exchanges: ½ starch, 1½ fruit, 1 fat

Baking Tip: Although you can make this recipe with peeled apples, leaving the
peels on ensures that you get more fiber, as well as the beneficial antioxidant quercetin.

Apricot-Plum Slump

2¼ *pounds ripe plums, pitted and cut into wedges*
⅔ *cup dried apricot halves*
¼ *cup + 3 tablespoons sugar*
⅓ *cup white grape juice*
2 *tablespoons honey*
1 *tablespoon lemon juice*
1¾ *cups whole grain pastry flour*
1 *teaspoon baking powder*
½ *teaspoon baking soda*
⅛ *teaspoon salt*
3 *tablespoons chilled butter, cut into small pieces*
¾ *cup low-fat buttermilk or fat-free plain yogurt*
⅛ *teaspoon ground cinnamon*

In a large deep skillet, mix the plums, apricots, ¼ cup of the sugar, the grape juice, honey, and lemon juice. Bring to a boil over medium-high heat. Reduce the heat to medium-low, cover, and simmer for 8 to 10 minutes, or until the fruit is fairly tender but not mushy.

In a food processor, combine the flour, baking powder, baking soda, salt, and 2 tablespoons of the remaining sugar. Pulse to blend.

Add the butter and pulse until fine crumbs form. Add the buttermilk or yogurt and pulse just until a soft dough forms.

In a cup, stir together the cinnamon and the remaining 1 tablespoon sugar.

Drop the dough by heaping tablespoons onto the hot fruit mixture. Sprinkle with the cinnamon sugar. Bring to a boil over medium heat, cover, and reduce the heat to medium-low. Simmer for 10 to 15 minutes, or until the dumplings are firm to the touch.

Remove from the heat, uncover, and let cool briefly before serving.

Makes 8 servings

Per serving: 292 calories, 5 g protein, 59 g carbohydrates, 5 g fat, 3 g saturated fat, 10 mg cholesterol, 240 mg sodium, 4 g dietary fiber

Exchanges: 1½ starch, 1½ fruit, 1 other carbohydrate, 1 fat

Baking Tip: Usually made with blueberries, a slump is an old New England dish with a less-than-elegant name that belies its luscious flavor. You'll appreciate this recipe in hot weather: No oven is needed because the slump cooks in a skillet on the stove. It's best to use a high-domed lid on the skillet to allow space for the dumplings to rise. If you don't have one, coat a regular lid with cooking spray so the dumplings won't stick to it.

Strawberry-Rhubarb Slump

Filling

⅔   cup sugar

2½   tablespoons cornstarch

¼   teaspoon ground cinnamon

1   package (10 ounces) frozen strawberries (packed in syrup), thawed

1   package (16 ounces) frozen cut rhubarb, thawed

Dumplings

1¼   cups unbleached flour

2   tablespoons sugar

1   teaspoon baking powder

¼   teaspoon baking soda

⅛   teaspoon salt

1½   tablespoons canola oil

1½   tablespoons nondiet tub-style margarine or butter, cut into small pieces

½   cup buttermilk

To make the filling: In a Dutch oven or large ovenproof saucepan, combine the sugar, cornstarch, and cinnamon.

Drain the juice from the strawberries into the pan; set the strawberries aside. Stir the sugar mixture until smooth.

Stir in the rhubarb. Bring the mixture to a boil over medium-high heat. Boil for 2 minutes, or until the mixture thickens and turns clear. Remove from the heat and stir in the strawberries. Set aside.

To make the dumplings: In a large bowl, combine the flour, sugar, baking powder, baking soda, and salt. Add the oil and margarine or butter. Using a fork or pastry blender, mix until crumbly. Add the buttermilk and mix just until moistened.

Drop large spoonfuls of the dough over the fruit mixture, spacing them so that they don't touch each other. Cover with a lid or foil. Cook over medium heat for 10 minutes.

Preheat the oven to 375°F.

Uncover the pan and transfer it to the oven. Bake for 15 to 20 minutes, or until a wooden pick inserted in a dumpling comes out clean. Cool for 10 minutes before serving.

Makes 6 servings

Per serving: 307 calories, 4 g protein, 59 g carbohydrates, 7 g fat, 1 g saturated fat, 1 mg cholesterol, 245 mg sodium, 3 g dietary fiber

Exchanges: 1½ starch, ½ fruit, 1½ other carbohydrate, 1 fat

Pies *and* Tarts

Beef, fish, fowl, and vegetables were all common ingredients in early pies. The Romans went so far as to enclose live birds in pie shells to create elaborate showpieces for their guests. Thankfully, around the 16th century, someone thought to layer fruits and custards under those flaky, buttery crusts. Most pies and tarts are easy to make, easy to bake, and easy to take along to share with friends and family. Our recipes make traditional favorites even better by replacing hydrogenated shortening with a mixture of butter and canola oil and reducing the fat and calories in crusts by using graham crackers and high-fiber whole grain pastry flour.

Triple Dark Chocolate Mousse Pie

Crust

8   *whole sheets cinnamon graham crackers, finely crushed*

¼   *cup unsweetened cocoa powder*

¼   *cup butter, melted*

Mousse

1   *package (19 ounces) reduced-fat soft tofu, well drained*

1   *package (8 ounces) bittersweet chocolate, melted*

¼   *cup chocolate syrup*

3   *tablespoons confectioners' sugar*

2   *teaspoons vanilla extract*

Pasteurized liquid egg substitute to equal 4 egg whites

Fat-free frozen whipped topping

Chocolate curls

Raspberries (optional)

To make the crust: In a 9" pie plate, combine the graham cracker crumbs, cocoa powder, and butter until well blended. Press the mixture into the bottom and up the side of the pie plate. Set aside.

To make the mousse: In a food processor or blender, process the tofu until smooth. Add the melted chocolate, chocolate syrup, sugar, and vanilla extract. Combine until the mixture is smooth.

Using an electric mixer on high speed, beat the egg substitute until stiff peaks form. Fold the chocolate mixture into the egg mixture until smooth. Spoon the mixture into the prepared pie crust. Refrigerate for at least 3 hours, or until the pie is set.

Add the whipped topping, chocolate curls, and raspberries (if using) to the top of the pie.

Makes 8 servings

Per serving: 395 calories, 23 g protein, 35 g carbohydrates, 20 g fat, 10 g saturated fat, 161 mg cholesterol, 369 mg sodium, 3 g dietary fiber

Exchanges: ½ starch, 2 other carbohydrate, 3 fat, 2½ very lean meat

Cherry Pie

1½ cups unbleached flour

¼ teaspoon salt

2 tablespoons unsalted butter

2 tablespoons canola oil

2 ounces low-fat cream cheese

2 teaspoons lemon juice

2–5 tablespoons ice water

4 cups fresh tart cherries, pitted

⅔ cup maple syrup

3 tablespoons quick-cooking tapioca

½ teaspoon grated lemon rind

1 teaspoon ground cinnamon

Preheat the oven to 425°F. In a large bowl, combine the flour and salt. Cut in the butter, oil, and cream cheese.

In a cup, combine the lemon juice with 2 tablespoons of the ice water. Sprinkle over the crumbs and mix until the crumbs are moistened. Mix in the remaining ice water, 1 tablespoon at a time, until the crumbs resemble the texture of cottage cheese and can be pressed into a firm ball. Gather the mixture into a ball; press into a thick disk. Cover; refrigerate for 15 to 30 minutes. Reserve ⅓ cup of the pie dough. Roll the remaining dough out to an 11" circle. Gently place the dough in a 9" round nonstick pie pan. Firmly press the dough against the bottom and sides of the pan. Fold the edges under and crimp to form a rim. Pierce the bottom of the crust with a fork to prevent it from puffing up. Bake for 8 to 10 minutes, or until lightly browned. Remove from the oven and cool on a wire rack. Reduce the oven temperature to 375°F.

Roll the reserved dough out to ⅛" thickness. Using a cookie cutter or sharp knife, cut out decorative shapes, such as hearts or stars; set aside.

Meanwhile, in a large saucepan, combine the cherries, maple syrup, tapioca, lemon rind, and cinnamon. Let the mixture stand for 5 minutes. Place over medium heat. Cook and stir for 10 minutes, or until thickened. Pour the cherry filling into the prebaked pie crust. Gently place the cut-outs over the filling. Bake for 20 to 30 minutes.

Makes 8 servings

Per serving: 282 calories, 4 g protein, 50 g carbohydrates, 8 g fat, 3 g saturated fat, 12 mg cholesterol, 100 mg sodium, 2 g dietary fiber

Exchanges: 1 starch, ½ fruit, 1 other carbohydrate, 1½ fat

Apple Crumb Pie

Crust

1½	*cups unbleached flour*
¼	*teaspoon salt*
2	*tablespoons unsalted butter*
2	*tablespoons canola oil*
2	*ounces low-fat cream cheese*
2	*teaspoons lemon juice*
2–5	*tablespoons ice water*

Topping

¾	*cup unbleached flour*
2	*tablespoons nondiet tub-style margarine or butter*
¼	*cup packed brown sugar*
¼	*teaspoon ground cinnamon*
⅛	*teaspoon ground nutmeg*

Filling

6	*Granny Smith apples, peeled, cored, and sliced*
1	*tablespoon lemon juice*
½	*cup sugar*
2½	*tablespoons quick-cooking tapioca*
½	*teaspoon ground cinnamon*
⅛	*teaspoon ground cloves*

Preheat the oven to 425°F.

To make the crust: In a large bowl, combine the flour and salt. Cut in the butter, oil, and cream cheese until the mixture resembles coarse crumbs.

In a cup, combine the lemon juice with 2 tablespoons of the ice water. Sprinkle over the crumbs and mix until the crumbs are moistened. Mix in the remaining ice water, 1 tablespoon at a time, until the crumbs resemble the texture of cottage cheese and can be pressed into a firm ball. Gather the mixture into a ball and press into a thick disk. Cover and refrigerate for 15 to 30 minutes before rolling out.

For a 9" single-crust pie, roll the dough out to a 12" circle. Gently place the dough in a 9" nonstick pie pan. Firmly press the dough against the bottom and sides of the pan. Fold the edges under and crimp to form a rim. Using a fork, pierce the bottom of the crust all over to prevent it from puffing up during baking.

To make the topping: Place the flour in a medium bowl. Using a pastry blender or table knives, cut in the margarine or butter until the mixture resembles coarse crumbs. Add the brown sugar, cinnamon, and nutmeg. Mix until well blended; set aside.

To make the filling: In a large bowl, combine the apples and lemon juice; set aside.

In a small bowl, combine the sugar, tapioca, cinnamon, and cloves. Sprinkle over the apples and gently toss to coat.

Spoon into the prepared pie crust. Sprinkle with the crumb topping.

Bake for 10 minutes. Reduce the oven temperature to 350°F and bake for 30 minutes, or until golden brown.

Makes 8 servings

Per serving: 360 calories, 5 g protein, 62 g carbohydrates, 11 g fat, 3 g saturated fat, 12 mg cholesterol, 136 mg sodium, 2 g dietary fiber

Exchanges: 2 starch, 1 fruit, 1 other carbohydrate, 2 fat

Variations

Pear Pie: Replace the apples with 8 Anjou pears.

Per serving: 436 calories, 5 g protein, 83 g carbohydrates, 11 g fat, 3 g saturated fat, 12 mg cholesterol, 138 mg sodium, 4 g dietary fiber

Exchanges: 2 starch, 2 fruit, 1 other carbohydrate, 2 fat

Phyllo-Top Apple Pie: Omit the crumb topping. Instead, coat one sheet of thawed phyllo dough with cooking spray. Sprinkle with ½ teaspoon cinnamon and ½ teaspoon sugar. Top with a second sheet of phyllo. Coat with cooking spray. Place the phyllo topping over the filling. Using your hands, gently wrinkle and fit the topping into the pan without going over the edges. Using a sharp knife, cut slashes into the top.

Per serving: 238 calories, 3 g protein, 41 g carbohydrates, 8 g fat, 3 g saturated fat, 12 mg cholesterol, 119 mg sodium, 3 g dietary fiber

Exchanges: 1 starch, 1 fruit, 1 other carbohydrate, 1½ fat

Raspberry-Apple Pie: Add 1 package (10 ounces) frozen unsweetened raspberries to the apples and lemon juice.

Per serving: 383 calories, 5 g protein, 69 g carbohydrates, 11 g fat, 3 g saturated fat, 12 mg cholesterol, 137 mg sodium, 5 g dietary fiber

Exchanges: 2 starch, 1 fruit, 1 other carbohydrate, 2 fat

Apricot-Blackberry Pie

1½	cups unbleached flour
¼	teaspoon salt
2	tablespoons unsalted butter
2	tablespoons canola oil
2	ounces low-fat cream cheese
2	teaspoons + 1 tablespoon lemon juice
2–5	tablespoons ice water
¼	cup cornstarch
3	tablespoons quick-cooking tapioca
½	teaspoon ground cinnamon
⅔	cup sugar
2	cups sliced apricots
2	cups fresh or frozen unsweetened blackberries

Preheat the oven to 425°F.

In a large bowl, combine the flour and salt. Cut in the butter, oil, and cream cheese until the mixture resembles coarse crumbs.

In a cup, combine 2 teaspoons of the lemon juice with 2 tablespoons of the ice water. Sprinkle over the crumbs and mix until the crumbs are moistened. Mix in the remaining ice water, 1 tablespoon at a time, until the crumbs resemble the texture of cottage cheese and can be pressed into a firm ball. Gather the mixture into a ball and press into a thick disk. Cover and refrigerate for 15 to 30 minutes before rolling out.

For a 9" single-crust pie, roll the dough out to a 12" circle. Gently place the dough in a 9" nonstick pie pan. Firmly press the dough against the bottom and sides of the pan. Fold the edges under and crimp to form a rim. Using a fork, pierce the bottom of the crust all over to prevent it from puffing up during baking. Bake for 10 to 12 minutes, or until lightly browned. Remove from the oven and cool on a wire rack.

Reduce the oven heat to 375°F.

In a small bowl, combine the cornstarch, tapioca, and cinnamon. Add the sugar and mix well.

In a large bowl, gently toss the apricots and blackberries with the remaining 1 tablespoon lemon juice. Fold in the sugar mixture.

Pour the fruit into the pie crust. Place the pie on a baking sheet to catch any drips. Bake for 35 minutes, or until the filling is bubbly and the crust is lightly browned. Cool before serving.

Makes 8 servings

Per serving: 289 calories, 4 g protein, 51 g carbohydrates, 8 g fat, 3 g saturated fat, 12 mg cholesterol, 96 mg sodium, 3 g dietary fiber

Exchanges: 1½ starch, ½ fruit, 1 other carbohydrate, 1½ fat

Variation

Peach-Berry Pie: *Replace the apricots with 2 cups sliced peaches and the blackberries with 2 cups fresh or frozen raspberries, blueberries, or strawberries.*

Per serving: 286 calories, 4 g protein, 51 g carbohydrates, 8 g fat, 3 g saturated fat, 12 mg cholesterol, 96 mg sodium, 3 g dietary fiber

Exchanges: 1½ starch, ½ fruit, 1 other carbohydrate, 1½ fat

Lemon Icebox Pie

1   cup (8 ounces) fat-free plain yogurt
6   whole graham crackers
1   tablespoon canola oil
¼   cup cornstarch
½   cup + 1 tablespoon honey
2   cups (16 ounces) low-fat vanilla yogurt
½   cup liquid egg substitute
½   cup lemon juice
½   teaspoon lemon extract
¼   teaspoon almond extract
3   egg whites, at room temperature
½   teaspoon cream of tartar
1   teaspoon vanilla extract

Line a sieve with a coffee filter or a white paper towel and place over a deep bowl. Place the plain yogurt in the sieve. Cover with plastic wrap, refrigerate, and allow to drain for 4 hours, or until very thick. Discard the liquid in the bowl.

Preheat the oven to 350°F. Coat a 10" pie plate with cooking spray.

Crumble the graham crackers into a food processor. Pulse to make crumbs. Add the oil and process to combine. Press the crumbs into the bottom and up the sides of the prepared pie plate to make a crust.

In a medium saucepan, whisk together the cornstarch and ½ cup of the honey. Whisk in the vanilla yogurt and the drained plain yogurt. Cook over medium heat, stirring constantly, for 5 minutes, or until the mixture comes to a boil and thickens.

Remove from the heat. Very slowly whisk in the egg substitute. Reduce the heat to low. Cook, stirring constantly, for 2 minutes. Remove from the heat and whisk in the lemon juice, lemon extract, and almond extract. Spoon into the prepared crust.

Combine the egg whites and cream of tartar in a medium bowl. Using an electric mixer on medium speed, beat until foamy. Add the vanilla extract and the remaining 1 tablespoon honey. Beat on high speed until stiff, glossy peaks form.

Spread over the pie filling, making sure to leave no gaps where the topping meets the crust.

Bake for 10 minutes, or until golden brown. Cool on a rack for 15 minutes. Refrigerate for at least 2 hours before serving.

Makes 8 servings

Per serving: 229 calories, 7 g protein, 44 g carbohydrates, 3 g fat, 1 g saturated fat, 6 mg cholesterol, 125 mg sodium, 0 g dietary fiber

Exchanges: 1 starch, 2 other carbohydrate, ½ very lean meat, ½ fat

Key Lime Pie

Photograph
on page 69

Crust

1	egg white
30	gingersnaps, finely crushed
1½	tablespoons butter, melted
1½	tablespoons canola oil

Filling

½	cup fresh lime juice
1	tablespoon grated lime rind
1	can (14 ounces) fat-free sweetened condensed milk
2	egg yolks
½	cup sugar
1	teaspoon cornstarch
4	egg whites, at room temperature
¼	teaspoon cream of tartar

Preheat the oven to 375°F. Coat a 9" pie plate with cooking spray.

To make the crust: Place the egg white in a medium bowl and beat lightly with a fork. Add the gingersnaps, butter, and oil. Mix well. Press the crumbs into the bottom and up the sides of the prepared pie plate to make a crust.

Bake for 8 to 10 minutes, or until lightly browned and firm. Cool on a wire rack.

To make the filling: In a large bowl, combine the lime juice and lime rind. Whisk in the condensed milk and egg yolks.

In a small bowl, mix the sugar and cornstarch.

Combine the egg whites and cream of tartar in a medium bowl. Using an electric mixer on medium speed, beat until foamy. Increase the speed to high and gradually beat in the sugar mixture. Beat until stiff, glossy peaks form.

Fold ¾ cup of the egg whites into the lime mixture. Pour into the prepared crust. Bake for 15 minutes. Remove from the oven.

Spoon the remaining egg whites over the filling and spread to the edges, making sure to leave no gaps where the topping meets the crust.

Bake for 10 minutes, or until golden brown. (If the topping browns too quickly, reduce the oven temperature to 350°F.) Cool on a rack. Refrigerate for 1 to 2 hours before serving.

Makes 8 servings

Per serving: 390 calories, 8 g protein, 62 g carbohydrates, 13 g fat, 5 g saturated fat, 75 mg cholesterol, 290 mg sodium, 1 g dietary fiber

Exchanges: 4 other carbohydrate, ½ very lean meat, 2 fat

Baking Tip: You can substitute ½ cup bottled Key lime juice for the fresh lime juice. Key limes are grown in the Florida Keys and have a more intense lime flavor than regular limes. Look for Key lime juice in the international aisle of your supermarket.

Fresh Blueberry Pie

2⅓   cups unbleached flour

3   teaspoons baking powder

⅓   cup canola oil

½   cup fat-free milk

1   cup sugar

½   teaspoon grated lemon rind

½   teaspoon ground cinnamon

4   cups fresh blueberries

Preheat the oven to 425°F. Coat a 9" nonstick pie pan with cooking spray.

In a medium bowl, whisk 2 cups of the flour with the baking powder. Alternately add the oil and milk, stirring until the dough forms a ball.

Divide the dough in half. Place one half of the dough on a large piece of waxed paper. Top with another large sheet of waxed paper. Roll out to a 12" circle. Remove the top sheet of paper and gently invert the dough into the prepared pan. Remove the remaining sheet of waxed paper. Firmly press the dough against the bottom and sides of the pan. Trim the dough that extends beyond the edge of the pan. Add the trimmed pieces to the remaining dough. Roll the dough out to a 12" circle between the waxed paper; set aside.

In a large bowl, gently mix the sugar, lemon rind, cinnamon, blueberries, and the remaining ⅓ cup flour. Pour the filling into the pie shell.

Remove the top sheet of waxed paper and carefully invert the top crust over the pie filling. Fold the edges under. Seal and crimp to form a rim. Using a sharp knife, make slits in the top.

To prevent overbrowning, cover the edge of the crust with a 1½"-wide strip of foil. Bake for 20 minutes. Remove the foil and bake for 15 to 20 minutes, or until golden brown and bubbly. Cool slightly before serving.

Makes 8 servings

Per serving: 361 calories, 5 g protein, 65 g carbohydrates, 10 g fat, 1 g saturated fat, 0 mg cholesterol, 192 mg sodium, 3 g dietary fiber

Exchanges: 1½ starch, ½ fruit, 1½ other carbohydrate, 2 fat

Pineapple Chiffon Pie with Strawberry Sauce

4   *sheets (13" x 9" each) frozen phyllo dough, thawed*

1   *package (4-serving-size) sugar-free pineapple gelatin*

½   *cup boiling water*

1   *can (12 ounces) fat-free evaporated milk*

⅓   *cup frozen pineapple juice concentrate, thawed*

2½   *cups sliced strawberries*

1   *tablespoon maple syrup or thawed pineapple juice concentrate*

Preheat the oven to 375°F. Coat a 9" pie plate with cooking spray.

Drape 1 sheet of the phyllo dough across the pie plate and fold the overhanging edges toward the center, crumpling them slightly to fit. Lightly mist the dough with cooking spray. Repeat to use all the sheets, placing each sheet at a 45-degree angle to the previous sheet and misting each with cooking spray.

Bake for 5 to 7 minutes, or until golden brown. Cool on a rack.

In a large bowl, stir together the gelatin and boiling water until the gelatin dissolves. Stir in the milk and pineapple juice concentrate. Cover and refrigerate for at least 30 minutes, or until the mixture mounds when dropped from a spoon.

Using an electric mixer on high speed, beat the gelatin mixture for 5 minutes, or until fluffy. Pour into the crust. Cover and refrigerate for 2 to 2½ hours, or until set.

Place 1½ cups of the strawberries and the maple syrup or pineapple juice concentrate in a blender. Process on medium speed until smooth. Place in a small bowl. Stir in the remaining 1 cup strawberries. Refrigerate until needed.

Cut the pie into wedges and spoon the strawberry sauce over each serving.

Makes 8 servings

Per serving: 107 calories, 6 g protein, 20 g carbohydrates, 1 g fat, 0 g saturated fat, 2 mg cholesterol, 142 mg sodium, 1 g dietary fiber

Exchanges: ½ starch, ½ fruit, ½ milk

Four-Berry Pie

Crust

2	cups whole grain pastry flour
½	teaspoon salt
4	tablespoons chilled butter, cut into small pieces
¼	cup canola oil
6	tablespoons fat-free sour cream
1–1½	tablespoons ice water
¼	teaspoon almond extract

Filling

2	cups halved strawberries
2	cups raspberries
1	cup blackberries
1	cup blueberries
3	tablespoons lemon juice
¾–1	cup sugar, depending on sweetness of fruit
3	tablespoons cornstarch
3	tablespoons instant tapioca

To make the crust: In a food processor, combine the flour and salt. Pulse until blended. Add the butter and oil. Pulse until the mixture resembles coarse crumbs.

Add the sour cream, 1 tablespoon of the ice water, and the almond extract. Pulse just until the dough forms large clumps. (If the dough seems too dry, add a few more drops of ice water.) Form into 2 equal balls and flatten each into a disk. Cover and refrigerate for at least 15 minutes or up to 1 day.

Preheat the oven to 400°F. Coat a 9" pie plate with cooking spray. Line a baking sheet with foil.

On a well-floured surface, roll out each piece of dough into a 10" circle. Fit 1 circle into the prepared pie plate, leaving the overhang. Slide the remaining circle onto a flat plate. Cover the dough and refrigerate until needed.

To make the filling: In a large bowl, mix the strawberries, raspberries, blackberries, blueberries, and lemon juice.

In a small bowl, mix the sugar, cornstarch, and tapioca. Sprinkle over the fruit, mix well, and let stand at room temperature for 15 minutes. Spoon into the pie plate.

Cut the remaining dough into ¾"-wide strips. Place half of the strips over the filling, spacing them evenly. Place the remaining strips at an opposing angle to the first strips to form a lattice pattern. Trim the ends of the lattice strips and the bottom crust to a ½" overhang, then fold the bottom crust over the lattice ends, and flute.

Place the pie on the prepared baking sheet and bake for 45 to 50 minutes, or until the crust is golden brown and the juices bubble. Cool on a rack.

Makes 8 servings

Per serving: 281 calories, 4 g protein, 55 g carbohydrates, 7 g fat, 4 g saturated fat, 15 mg cholesterol, 221 mg sodium, 6 g dietary fiber

Exchanges: 1½ starch, 1 fruit, 1 other carbohydrate, 1 fat

Ginger Pumpkin Pie

*Photograph
on page 141*

Crust

1¼	cups whole grain pastry flour
¼	teaspoon salt
3	tablespoons canola oil
2	tablespoons chilled butter, cut into small pieces
2–4	tablespoons ice water

Filling

½	cup packed light brown sugar
1	egg
2	egg whites
1½	teaspoons vanilla extract
½	teaspoon ground cinnamon
½	teaspoon ground ginger
¼	teaspoon ground nutmeg
⅛	teaspoon salt
1	can (15 ounces) plain pumpkin
1	cup fat-free evaporated milk

To make the crust: In a food processor, combine the flour and the salt. Pulse until blended. Add the oil and butter. Pulse until the mixture resembles coarse crumbs.

Add the water, 1 tablespoon at a time, and pulse just until the dough forms large clumps. Form into a ball and flatten into a disk. Cover and refrigerate for at least 1 hour.

Preheat the oven to 425°F. Coat a 9" pie plate with cooking spray.

Place the dough between 2 pieces of waxed paper and roll into a 12" circle. Remove the top piece of paper and invert the dough into the pie plate. Peel off the second piece of paper. Press the dough into the pie plate and up onto the rim, patching where necessary. Turn under the rim and flute. Refrigerate until needed.

To make the filling: In a large bowl, whisk the brown sugar, egg, egg whites, vanilla extract, cinnamon, ginger, nutmeg, and the salt until well blended. Whisk in the pumpkin and milk. Pour into the prepared crust.

Bake for 15 minutes. Reduce the temperature to 350°F. Bake for 25 minutes, or until a knife inserted near the center comes out clean. Cool on a rack.

Makes 8 servings

Per serving: 268 calories, 6 g protein, 42 g carbohydrates, 9 g fat, 2 g saturated fat, 34 mg cholesterol, 326 mg sodium, 6 g dietary fiber

Exchanges: ½ starch, ½ milk, 1½ other carbohydrate, 2 fat

Shoofly Pie

3	cups unbleached flour
¼	teaspoon salt
2	tablespoons unsalted butter
2	ounces fat-free cream cheese
2	teaspoons lemon juice
2–5	tablespoons ice water
2	tablespoons nondiet tub-style margarine or butter
½	cup packed Splenda Brown Sugar Blend
1	teaspoon ground cinnamon
1	cup boiling water
1	teaspoon baking soda
1	cup Barbados molasses or regular light molasses
¼	teaspoon ground ginger

In a large bowl, combine 1½ cups of the flour and the salt. Cut in the butter and cream cheese until the mixture resembles coarse crumbs.

In a cup, combine the lemon juice with 2 tablespoons of the ice water. Sprinkle over the crumbs and mix until the crumbs are moistened. Mix in the remaining ice water, 1 tablespoon at a time, until the crumbs resemble the texture of cottage cheese and can be pressed into a firm ball. Gather the mixture into a ball and press into a thick disk. Cover and refrigerate for 15 to 30 minutes before rolling out.

For a 9" single-crust pie, roll the dough out to a 12" circle. Spray a 9" nonstick pie pan with cooking spray. Gently place the dough in the pan. Firmly press the dough against the bottom and sides of the pan. Fold the edges under and crimp to form a rim. Using a fork, pierce the bottom of the crust all over to prevent it from puffing up during baking.

Place the remaining 1½ cups flour in a medium bowl. Using a pastry blender or table knives, cut in the margarine or butter until the mixture resembles coarse crumbs. Mix in the brown sugar and cinnamon until well blended. Set aside.

Preheat the oven to 450°F.

In another medium bowl, whisk the boiling water and baking soda until the baking soda dissolves. Stir in the molasses and ginger. Mix well. Allow the mixture to cool slightly. Pour into the unbaked pie crust. Sprinkle evenly with the crumb mixture.

Bake for 10 minutes. Reduce the heat to 350°F and bake for 30 to 40 minutes, or until the center of the filling is set and the crumbs are golden brown.

Makes 8 servings

Per serving: 333 calories, 6 g protein, 63 g carbohydrates, 5 g fat, 2 g saturated fat, 7 mg cholesterol, 295 mg sodium, 1 g dietary fiber

Exchanges: 1½ starch, 1½ other carbohydrate, 1 fat

Variation

For a tasty topping, spoon 2 tablespoons of fat-free vanilla frozen yogurt over each slice of pie.

Per serving: 358 calories, 7 g protein, 69 g carbohydrates, 5 g fat, 2 g saturated fat, 8 mg cholesterol, 312 mg sodium, 1 g dietary fiber

Exchanges: 1½ starch, 1½ other carbohydrate, 1 fat

Cheesecake Tart

4	tablespoons apricot jelly
2½	cups graham cracker crumbs
1	container (15 ounces) part-skim ricotta cheese
2	cups (16 ounces) fat-free plain yogurt
⅓	cup honey
3	tablespoons cornstarch
2	tablespoons lime juice
1	tablespoon vanilla extract
3	cups fruit, such as halved strawberries, sliced bananas, and/or blueberries

Preheat the oven to 350°F. Coat an 8" pie plate with cooking spray.

Melt 2 tablespoons of the jelly in a small saucepan over low heat. Remove from the heat, add the crumbs, and mix well. Press into the bottom and up the sides of the pie plate to make a crust.

Place the ricotta in a food processor and process until very smooth. Add the yogurt, honey, cornstarch, lime juice, and vanilla extract. Process for about 30 seconds, or until well mixed. Pour into the prepared crust.

Bake for 30 to 40 minutes, or until a knife inserted in the center comes out clean. Cool on a rack for 30 minutes. Refrigerate for at least 3 hours.

Just before serving, melt the remaining 2 tablespoons jelly in a medium saucepan. Remove from the heat. Stir in the fruit and mix well. Top the cheesecake with the fruit.

Makes 8 servings

Per serving: 341 calories, 11 g protein, 59 g carbohydrates, 7 g fat, 3 g saturated fat, 17 mg cholesterol, 273 mg sodium, 2 g dietary fiber

Exchanges: 1½ starch, ½ fruit, 2 other carbohydrate, 1 lean meat, 1 fat

Apricot Tart

1½ cups unbleached flour

1 tablespoon sugar

¼ teaspoon salt

2 tablespoons unsalted butter

2 ounces fat-free cream cheese

2 teaspoons lemon juice

4 tablespoons ice water

2 tablespoons apricot brandy or reserved apricot juice

¾ cup apricot all-fruit spread, warmed

4 cans (16 ounces each) apricot halves, drained and juice reserved

2 tablespoons toasted slivered almonds

Preheat the oven to 425°F.

In a large bowl, combine the flour, sugar, and salt. Cut in the butter and cream cheese.

In a cup, combine the lemon juice with 2 tablespoons of the ice water. Sprinkle over the crumbs and toss with a fork until the crumbs resemble the texture of cottage cheese. Mix in the remaining ice water, 1 tablespoon at a time, until the dough holds together. Gather the mixture into a ball and press into a thick disk. Cover and refrigerate for 30 minutes.

For an 11" tart, roll the dough out to a 12" circle. Spray a tart pan with cooking spray. Gently place the dough in the pan. Firmly press the dough against the bottom and sides of the pan. Fold the edges under. Using a fork, pierce the bottom of the crust all over to prevent it from puffing up during baking. Bake for 10 to 12 minutes, or until lightly browned. Remove from the oven and cool on a wire rack.

Reduce the oven heat to 350°F.

Stir the brandy or apricot juice into the all-fruit spread. Using a pastry brush, brush a thin layer of the fruit spread mixture over the prebaked tart crust. Arrange a single layer of the apricot halves, cut side down, in the crust. Brush the apricots with fruit spread. Continue layering with apricot halves and brushing with fruit spread until they are all used. Sprinkle with the almonds. Bake for 15 minutes. Cool on a wire rack before serving.

Makes 8 servings

Per serving: 257 calories, 6 g protein, 49 g carbohydrates, 4 g fat, 2 g saturated fat, 9 mg cholesterol, 175 mg sodium, 3 g dietary fiber

Exchanges: 1 starch, 1 fruit, 1 other carbohydrate, ½ fat

Strawberry Meringue Tart

¼   cup cornstarch

¼   cup finely ground blanched almonds

¾   cup sugar

3   egg whites, at room temperature

⅛   teaspoon cream of tartar

    Pinch of salt

1   teaspoon vanilla extract

1½   pints strawberries

2   tablespoons seedless raspberry all-fruit preserves

2   teaspoons water

Preheat the oven to 300°F. Line a baking sheet with parchment paper or foil and coat lightly with cooking spray.

In a small bowl, mix the cornstarch, almonds, and ¼ cup of the sugar.

Place the egg whites, cream of tartar, and salt in a large bowl. Using an electric mixer on medium speed, beat until soft peaks form. With the mixer at medium-high speed, slowly add the remaining ½ cup sugar and beat until stiff, glossy peaks form. Beat in the vanilla extract. Gently fold in the almond mixture.

Using a large spoon, spread enough of the egg white mixture on the baking sheet to form an 8" or 9" circle about ¾" thick. Drop spoonfuls of the remaining whites around the edge to form a border about 1" high. (Or use a pastry bag fitted with a large rosette tip to pipe a fancier border.)

Bake on the bottom rack of the oven for 30 minutes, or until light tan and crisp. Cool on a rack for 5 minutes. Carefully peel off the paper or foil.

Place the shell on a serving plate. Fill with the strawberries.

Place the preserves and water in a small saucepan. Melt over low heat. Using a pastry brush, lightly glaze the strawberries with the melted preserves. Serve the tart at room temperature.

Makes 8 servings

Per serving: 150 calories, 3 g protein, 30 g carbohydrates, 3 g fat, 0 g saturated fat, 0 mg cholesterol, 23 mg sodium, 2 g dietary fiber

Exchanges: ½ starch, ½ fruit, 1½ other carbohydrate, ½ very lean meat, ½ fat

Baking Tip: This elegant confection has a meringue shell rather than a pastry crust. The chewy meringue bakes more quickly, and in a hotter oven, than traditional meringues, emerging a delicate tan rather than pure white.

Kiwi Custard Tart

Crust

1	cup whole grain pastry flour
1	teaspoon sugar
½	teaspoon grated lemon rind
¼	teaspoon salt
2	tablespoons canola oil
2	tablespoons chilled butter, cut into small pieces
3	tablespoons fat-free sour cream
2–2½	teaspoons ice water

Filling

1¼	cups 1% milk
1	teaspoon grated lemon rind
¼	cup sugar
2	tablespoons cornstarch
	Pinch of salt
1	egg
1	egg white
1	teaspoon vanilla extract
5	kiwifruit, peeled and sliced ¼" thick

To make the crust: In a food processor, combine the flour, sugar, lemon rind, and salt. Pulse until blended. Add the oil and butter. Pulse until the mixture resembles coarse crumbs.

Add the sour cream and 2 teaspoons of the ice water. Pulse just until the dough forms large clumps. (Add a few drops of water if the dough seems dry.) Form into a ball and flatten into a disk. Cover and refrigerate for at least 15 minutes.

Preheat the oven to 400°F.

On a lightly floured surface, roll the dough into a 10" round. Place in a 9" tart pan and gently press it into the bottom and sides of the pan. Trim the edges and prick the bottom with a fork. Place in the freezer for 5 minutes, then line the crust with foil and fill it with pie weights.

Bake for 8 to 10 minutes. Remove the weights and foil. Bake for 5 minutes. Transfer to a rack to cool for 10 minutes. Do not turn off the oven.

To make the filling: In a medium saucepan, bring the milk and lemon rind just to a simmer over medium-high heat. Remove from the heat.

In a medium bowl, mix the sugar, cornstarch, and salt. Whisk in the egg and egg white. Gradually whisk in the hot milk and vanilla extract. Pour into the cooled tart shell.

Bake for 15 minutes, or until set. Cool on a rack for at least 20 minutes.

Arrange the kiwifruit on top of the custard, starting from the outside edge. Serve at room temperature.

Makes 8 servings

Per serving: 192 calories, 5 g protein, 27 g carbohydrates, 8 g fat, 3 g saturated fat, 36 mg cholesterol, 140 mg sodium, 3 g dietary fiber

Exchanges: ½ starch, ½ fruit, ½ milk, ½ other carbohydrate, 1½ fat

Raspberry-Almond Tart

Crust

*Photograph
on page 143*

⅔   *cup old-fashioned rolled oats*

½   *cup whole grain pastry flour*

1   *tablespoon sugar*

1   *teaspoon ground cinnamon*

¼   *teaspoon baking soda*

2   *tablespoons canola oil*

2–3   *tablespoons fat-free plain yogurt*

⅓   *cup miniature semisweet chocolate chips*

Filling

¼   *cup raspberry all-fruit preserves*

¾   *teaspoon almond extract*

2½   *cups raspberries*

2   *tablespoons sliced almonds*

To make the crust: Preheat the oven to 375°F. Coat a baking sheet with cooking spray.

In a medium bowl, mix the oats, flour, sugar, cinnamon, and baking soda. Stir in the oil and 2 tablespoons of the yogurt to make a soft, slightly sticky dough. If the dough is too stiff, add the remaining 1 tablespoon yogurt.

Place the dough on the prepared baking sheet. With lightly oiled hands, pat evenly into a 10" circle. Place a 9" cake pan in the middle of the dough and trace around it with a sharp knife, being careful only to score the surface of the dough. With your fingers, push up and pinch the dough around the outside of the pan to make a 9" crust with a rim ¼" high. Remove the cake pan.

Bake for 12 minutes. Scatter the chocolate chips evenly over the surface of the crust. Bake for 3 to 4 minutes, or until the chocolate is melted and the crust is firm and golden. Remove from the oven and spread the chocolate over the crust to make an even layer. Cool on a rack.

To make the filling: In a small microwaveable bowl, mix the preserves and almond extract. Microwave on high power for 10 to 15 seconds, or until melted. Brush a generous tablespoon evenly over the crust. Top with the raspberries. Brush the remaining preserves evenly over the berries, making sure to get some between the berries to secure them. Sprinkle with the almonds.

Refrigerate for at least 30 minutes, or until the preserves have jelled.

Makes 8 servings

Per serving: 173 calories, 3 g protein, 25 g carbohydrates, 8 g fat, 2 g saturated fat, 1 mg cholesterol, 44 mg sodium, 5 g dietary fiber

Exchanges: ½ starch, ½ fruit, 1½ other carbohydrate, 1½ fat

Rustic Plum-Walnut Tart

Crust

Photograph on page 142

1	cup whole grain pastry flour
¼	teaspoon salt
¼	teaspoon ground cinnamon
2	tablespoons canola oil
3–4	tablespoons ice water

Filling

⅓	cup + 1 teaspoon sugar
¼	cup Grape-Nuts or low-fat granola
2	tablespoons whole grain pastry flour
2	tablespoons chopped toasted walnuts
6	plums, pitted and quartered
1	tablespoon fat-free milk
2	tablespoons red currant jelly

To make the crust: Preheat the oven to 400°F. Line a baking sheet with foil and coat with cooking spray.

In a medium bowl, mix the flour, salt, and cinnamon. Using a fork, slowly stir in the oil until coarse crumbs form. Stir in enough ice water to form a slightly sticky dough. Form into a ball and flatten into a disk. Cover and refrigerate for 15 minutes.

Place the dough between 2 pieces of waxed paper and roll into a 12" circle. Remove the top piece of paper and invert the dough onto the prepared baking sheet. Peel off the second piece of paper.

To make the filling: In a food processor, combine ⅓ cup of the sugar, the cereal, flour, and walnuts. Pulse until finely ground.

Spread over the dough, leaving a 1½" border around the edge. Arrange the plums in concentric circles over the nut mixture. Fold the pastry border over the outside edge of the plums. Brush the milk over the dough and sprinkle with the remaining 1 teaspoon sugar.

Bake for 30 to 40 minutes, or until the crust is golden and the juices are bubbling. With a long metal spatula, loosen the pastry bottom. Slide the tart onto a serving platter and let cool.

Before serving, melt the jelly in a small saucepan over low heat. Brush over the plums.

Makes 8 servings

Per serving: 172 calories, 3 g protein, 32 g carbohydrates, 5 g fat, 0 g saturated fat, 0 mg cholesterol, 82 mg sodium, 2 g dietary fiber

Exchanges: 1 starch, ½ fruit, ½ other carbohydrate, 1 fat

Delicate Pear Tart

Tart Shell

1	cup whole grain pastry flour
¼	teaspoon salt
⅛	teaspoon ground nutmeg
2	tablespoons canola oil
2	tablespoons chilled butter, cut into small pieces
3	tablespoons fat-free sour cream
2–2½	teaspoons ice water

Filling

6	ripe pears, peeled, halved, cored, and thinly sliced
⅓	cup chopped walnuts
¼	cup packed light brown sugar
¼	cup apple jelly, melted

Preheat the oven to 350°F. Coat a 10" tart pan with cooking spray.

To make the shell: In a food processor, combine the flour, salt, and nutmeg. Pulse until blended. Add the oil and butter. Pulse until the mixture resembles coarse crumbs.

Add the sour cream and 2 teaspoons of the ice water. Pulse just until the dough forms large clumps. (Add a few drops of water if the dough seems dry.) Form into a ball and flatten into a disk. Cover and refrigerate for 15 minutes.

Roll the dough into an 11" circle. Place in the prepared pan. Firmly press the dough against the bottom and sides of the pan. Trim the edges.

To make the filling: Arrange the pears in the crust in a decorative pattern. Sprinkle with the walnuts and brown sugar.

Bake for 45 minutes, or until the pears are tender and the pastry is golden. Cool on a rack for 10 minutes. Brush with the jelly. Cool for at least 2 hours before serving.

Makes 12 servings

Per serving: 170 calories, 2 g protein, 28 g carbohydrates, 7 g fat, 2 g saturated fat, 5 mg cholesterol, 75 mg sodium, 3 g dietary fiber

Exchanges: ½ starch, 1 fruit, ½ other carbohydrate, 1½ fat

Gingersnap-Pear Tart

2 *cups gingersnap cookie crumbs*

1 *egg white*

8 *ounces reduced-fat cream cheese, at room temperature*

2 *tablespoons chopped crystallized ginger*

1 *tablespoon packed light brown sugar*

1 *can (16 ounces) pear halves in juice, drained and sliced*

2 *tablespoons apricot all-fruit preserves, melted*

Preheat the oven to 350°F. Coat a 10" tart pan with cooking spray.

In a small bowl, mix the crumbs and egg white until well blended. Press onto the bottom and up the sides of the prepared pan.

Bake for 15 minutes, or until set. Cool on a rack.

In a medium bowl, combine the cream cheese, ginger, and brown sugar. Using an electric mixer on medium speed, beat for 2 minutes, or until fluffy.

Spread over the tart shell and top with the pears. Brush with the preserves.

Makes 12 servings

Per serving: 98 calories, 3 g protein, 13 g carbohydrates, 4 g fat, 2 g saturated fat, 11 mg cholesterol, 100 mg sodium, 1 g dietary fiber

Exchanges: ½ fruit, ½ other carbohydrate, ½ lean meat, ½ fat

Summer Dessert Pizza

Crust

1½ cups whole grain pastry flour

2 tablespoons sugar

3 tablespoons chilled butter, cut into small pieces

1 egg yolk

3 tablespoons fat-free milk

Topping

4 ounces reduced-fat cream cheese, at room temperature

3 tablespoons confectioners' sugar

1 cup (8 ounces) low-fat vanilla yogurt

½ teaspoon vanilla extract

2 cups sliced strawberries

1 cup blueberries

1 kiwifruit, peeled, halved lengthwise, and thinly sliced

1 tablespoon currant or apple jelly, melted

To make the crust: Line a baking sheet with foil and coat with cooking spray.

In a food processor, combine the flour and sugar. Pulse to mix. Add the butter and process just until the mixture resembles fine crumbs.

In a small bowl, whisk together the egg yolk and milk. Add to the food processor and pulse until the dough forms large clumps.

On a lightly floured work surface, pat the dough into a flattened disk. Place between 2 pieces of waxed paper and roll into a 10" circle. Remove the top piece of paper and invert the dough onto the prepared baking sheet. Refrigerate for 30 minutes. Peel off the second piece of paper.

Preheat the oven to 350°F.

Bake the dough for 15 minutes, or until just golden. Cool on a rack. Remove from the foil.

To make the topping: In a small bowl, mix the cream cheese and sugar until smooth. Stir in the yogurt and vanilla extract.

Spread over the cooled crust, leaving a ¼" border. Decoratively arrange the strawberries, blueberries, and kiwifruit over the filling. Brush with the jelly.

Makes 8 servings

Per serving: 225 calories, 6 g protein, 34 g carbohydrates, 8 g fat, 5 g saturated fat, 48 mg cholesterol, 109 mg sodium, 3 g dietary fiber

Exchanges: ½ starch, ½ fruit, 1 other carbohydrate, 1½ fat

Puddings
and Mousses

Puddings of all sorts have been around for centuries, although most weren't as sweet and appetizing as those we delight in today. Smooth, creamy, and delicious, pudding makes a yummy snack any time of day. Although you will find your old favorites such as tapioca, rice, and chocolate pudding, we've also added some new flavors for you to enjoy. Don't be afraid to try them all. We've used cocoa powder in place of chocolate and substituted 2% milk for high-fat cream, making a delightful treat for the diabetic diet. Still satisfying and delicious, these snacks remain rich in flavor but low in sugar.

Tapioca Pudding

3   tablespoons quick-cooking tapioca

⅓   cup sugar

2   eggs

¼   teaspoon ground cardamom

¼   teaspoon ground cinnamon

4   cups fat-free milk

¼   cup dried cherries, blueberries, or raisins

1   teaspoon vanilla extract

In a medium saucepan, mix the tapioca, sugar, eggs, cardamom, and cinnamon until smooth. Stir in the milk. Bring to a boil over medium heat. Reduce the heat to low and simmer, stirring constantly, for 5 minutes.

Remove from the heat and stir in the cherries, blueberries, or raisins and vanilla extract. Pour into a serving bowl and cover the surface with plastic wrap. Refrigerate until cold.

Makes 8 servings

Per serving: 123 calories, 6 g protein, 21 g carbohydrates, 2 g fat, 1 g saturated fat, 55 mg cholesterol, 80 mg sodium, 0 g dietary fiber

Exchanges: ½ starch, ½ milk, ½ other carbohydrate, ½ lean meat

Hearty Rice Pudding

3	cups fat-free milk
½	cup uncooked brown rice
¼	cup + 1 teaspoon packed light brown sugar
1	teaspoon vanilla extract
⅛	teaspoon salt
⅛	teaspoon ground cinnamon
2	eggs
1	cup raspberries
	Mint sprigs (optional)

In a medium saucepan, mix the milk, rice, ¼ cup of the brown sugar, the vanilla extract, salt, and cinnamon. Bring to a boil over medium heat. Reduce the heat to low, cover, and simmer for 1½ hours. Remove from the heat and let cool for 5 minutes.

In a small bowl, lightly beat the eggs with a fork. Stir about ½ cup of the rice mixture into the eggs. Gradually stir the egg mixture into the saucepan.

Place over medium-low heat and cook, stirring constantly, for 5 minutes, or until thickened. Remove from the heat and cool for 10 minutes. Pour into a serving bowl and cover the surface with plastic wrap. Refrigerate until cold.

In a blender, process ½ cup of the raspberries until smooth. If desired, place in a sieve over a bowl and strain to remove the seeds. Stir in the remaining 1 teaspoon brown sugar. Cover and refrigerate.

To serve, spoon the pudding into dessert dishes, drizzle with the raspberry sauce, and top with the remaining ½ cup raspberries. Garnish with the mint (if using).

Makes 8 servings

Per serving: 122 calories, 6 g protein, 20 g carbohydrates, 2 g fat, 1 g saturated fat, 55 mg cholesterol, 112 mg sodium, 1 g dietary fiber

Exchanges: 1 starch, ½ milk

Homemade Vanilla Pudding with Fresh Berries

½   cup cornstarch

1   cup sugar

½   teaspoon salt

3   eggs

4   cups fat-free half-and-half

1   teaspoon vanilla extract

2   cups fresh berries of your choice (such as 1 cup raspberries and 1 cup blueberries)

In a medium bowl, combine the cornstarch, sugar, salt, and eggs and whisk until smooth.

In a large saucepan over medium heat, bring the half-and-half almost to a boil. With a ladle, transfer about 1½ cups at a time into the egg mixture, whisking quickly after each addition. (This will bring the eggs up to the temperature of the half-and-half without scrambling them.) When all of the half-and-half has been added to the eggs, transfer the entire mixture back to the saucepan and return it to the stove over medium heat. To prevent scorching, stir constantly with a wooden spoon. Be sure to scrape the entire bottom of the pot as the half-and-half returns to a boil. Continue stirring vigorously as the mixture thickens (It will appear chunky at this stage). Once the entire mixture is completely chunky and is spurting air, it is done.

Remove the saucepan from the heat and whisk in the vanilla extract. Transfer the pudding to a heatproof bowl and whisk periodically as it cools. Cover and refrigerate overnight. (For faster cooling, place in a bowl over another bowl filled with ice water and whisk periodically.) Just before serving, whisk once more, then fold in the berries.

Makes 8 servings

Per serving: 242 calories, 6 g protein, 48 g carbohydrates, 4 g fat, 2 g saturated fat, 76 mg cholesterol, 342 mg sodium, 2 g dietary fiber

Exchanges: ½ starch, ½ fruit, 1½ other carbohydrate, ½ fat, ½ meat

Variation

Lemon Pudding: Omit the berries. Replace the vanilla extract with lemon extract and add 1 tablespoon of grated lemon rind at the end.

Per serving: 224 calories, 5 g protein, 43 g carbohydrates, 3 g fat, 2 g saturated fat, 76 mg cholesterol, 342 mg sodium, 1 g dietary fiber

Exchanges: ½ starch, 1½ other carbohydrate, ½ fat, ½ meat

Old-Fashioned Chocolate Pudding

2   cups fat-free milk

¾   teaspoon instant espresso coffee powder

½   cup sugar

2   ounces bittersweet or semisweet chocolate, finely chopped

3   tablespoons cornstarch, sifted

In a 2-quart saucepan, scald 1¾ cups of the milk. Stir in the coffee powder and sugar until dissolved.

In the top of a double boiler, over gently simmering water, melt the chocolate. Gradually add the milk mixture, stirring until smooth. Continue to cook in the double boiler, stirring often.

In a cup, dissolve the cornstarch in the remaining ¼ cup milk. Gradually whisk the cornstarch mixture into the chocolate mixture. Whisk constantly for 5 minutes, or until the pudding is thickened.

Transfer the pudding to a serving dish. Cover with plastic wrap and refrigerate for at least 45 minutes before serving.

Makes 4 servings

Per serving: 234 calories, 5 g protein, 44 g carbohydrates, 6 g fat, 3 g saturated fat, 3 mg cholesterol, 64 mg sodium, 1 g dietary fiber

Exchanges: 1 fat, ½ milk, 2 carbohydrates, ½ starch

Variation

Mocha Chocolate Pudding: Increase the instant espresso coffee powder to 2 teaspoons.

Per serving: 234 calories, 5 g protein, 44 g carbohydrates, 6 g fat, 3 g saturated fat, 3 mg cholesterol, 64 mg sodium, 1 g dietary fiber

Exchanges: 1 fat, ½ milk, 2 carbohydrates, ½ starch

Chocolate Pudding Cups

Photograph
on page 147

8   *prepared crêpes*

4   *ounces reduced-fat cream cheese, cut into small pieces*

1   *cup fat-free milk or unsweetened soy milk*

1   *package (4-serving-size) sugar-free instant chocolate pudding mix*

3   *cups strawberries, sliced*

Preheat the oven to 400°F.

Invert eight 6-ounce custard cups on a baking sheet. Coat the outside of the cups with cooking spray. Drape a crêpe over each cup. Coat the crêpes with cooking spray.

Bake for 20 minutes. Turn off the oven and let the crêpes stand in the oven for 30 minutes, or until crisp. Carefully lift the crêpes from the custard cups and place on a rack to cool.

In a food processor or blender, combine the cream cheese, milk, and pudding mix. Process until smooth.

To serve, place each crêpe cup, right side up, on a dessert plate. Spoon a layer of strawberries in the bottom of each. Divide the pudding among the cups and top with the remaining strawberries.

Makes 8 servings

Per serving: 293 calories, 12 g protein, 29 g carbohydrates, 14 g fat, 5 g saturated fat, 170 mg cholesterol, 140 mg sodium, 2 g dietary fiber

Exchanges: 2 starch, 3 fat

Creamy Banana Pudding

¾ cup sweetened condensed milk

1 tablespoon + 1 teaspoon lemon juice

2 cups (16 ounces) fat-free vanilla yogurt

½ cup reduced-fat sour cream

1 teaspoon vanilla extract

⅓ cup cold water

1 envelope unflavored gelatin

4 large bananas

20 reduced-fat vanilla wafers

In a large bowl, whisk the condensed milk with 1 tablespoon of the lemon juice until slightly thickened. Whisk in the yogurt, sour cream, and vanilla extract until smooth.

Pour the water into a small saucepan. Sprinkle with the gelatin and let soften for 2 minutes. Cook over medium heat, stirring constantly, for 1 to 2 minutes, or until the gelatin is completely dissolved and the mixture is heated through. Stir into the yogurt mixture.

Slice 3 of the bananas into ¼" rounds. Drizzle with the remaining 1 teaspoon lemon juice. Fold into the pudding. Pour into 8 dessert glasses, cover, and refrigerate for at least 2 hours, or until the pudding is set.

To serve, thinly slice the remaining banana. Arrange the slices and the vanilla wafers on top of the pudding.

Makes 8 servings

Per serving: 274 calories, 8 g protein, 51 g carbohydrates, 5 g fat, 3 g saturated fat, 15 mg cholesterol, 115 mg sodium, 3 g dietary fiber

Exchanges: 1 fruit, 2 other carbohydrate, 1 fat

Amaretti Pudding

2   cups 2% milk
⅓   cup packed light brown sugar
¼   cup cornstarch
¼   teaspoon salt
½   cup fat-free milk
1   teaspoon vanilla extract
5   large amaretti cookies, crumbled

Place the 2% milk in a medium saucepan. Warm over medium heat just until small bubbles form around the edge. Remove from the heat.

In a medium bowl, mix the brown sugar, cornstarch, and salt. Gradually whisk in the fat-free milk until smooth. Whisk in the warm milk.

Pour into the saucepan and bring to a boil over medium heat, stirring constantly. Cook, stirring, for 1 minute, or until thickened. Remove from the heat and stir in the vanilla extract.

Spoon into 4 dessert dishes, cover, and refrigerate for 1½ hours, or until cold.

To serve, sprinkle with the amaretti crumbs.

Makes 4 servings
Per serving: 152 calories, 5 g protein, 24 g carbohydrates, 4 g fat, 2 g saturated fat, 10 mg cholesterol, 270 mg sodium, 0 g dietary fiber
Exchanges: ½ starch, ½ milk, ½ other carbohydrate, 1 fat

Baking Tip: Amaretti cookies are available at gourmet shops, Italian grocery stores, and many supermarkets; look for brightly colored tins or bags. If you can't find them, try another crisp topping, such as crumbled chocolate or vanilla wafers, your favorite breakfast cereal, or a few spoonfuls of toasted coconut.

Pecan-Topped Pumpkin Pudding

2 eggs, beaten

1 can (15 ounces) pumpkin

1 can (12 ounces) 2% evaporated milk

¾ cup Splenda Brown Sugar Blend

1 teaspoon ground cinnamon

¼ teaspoon ground nutmeg

¼ teaspoon ground cloves

¼ teaspoon ground ginger

½ teaspoon salt

1 teaspoon vanilla extract

8 teaspoons chopped pecans

Preheat the oven to 350°F. Spray 8 half-cup ramekins with cooking spray.

In a large bowl, mix the eggs, pumpkin, milk, brown sugar, cinnamon, nutmeg, cloves, ginger, salt, and vanilla extract. Divide the mixture among the ramekins.

Place the ramekins in a 13" x 9" baking dish with enough water to cover bottom of the baking dish. Bake for 45 minutes.

Remove from the oven. Sprinkle each pudding with 1 teaspoon of the chopped pecans. Serve warm or at room temperature.

Makes 8 servings

Per serving: 140 calories, 6 g protein, 19 g carbohydrates, 4 g fat, 1 g saturated fat, 56 mg cholesterol, 214 mg sodium, 2 g dietary fiber

Exchanges: ½ starch, ½ milk, ½ fat

Creamy Mousse with Concord Grape Sauce

1	cup reduced-fat ricotta cheese
⅔	cup fat-free plain yogurt
7	tablespoons confectioners' sugar
½	teaspoon grated lemon rind
½	teaspoon vanilla extract
¼	teaspoon ground cinnamon
2	tablespoons cold water
1	teaspoon unflavored gelatin
⅓	cup Concord grape juice
¾	teaspoon cornstarch
¼	cup toasted pecans, chopped

In a medium bowl, mix the ricotta, yogurt, sugar, lemon rind, vanilla extract, and cinnamon.

Place the water in a small saucepan. Sprinkle with the gelatin. Let stand for 1 minute to soften. Warm over very low heat, stirring constantly, for 1 minute, or until the gelatin is dissolved. Stir into the ricotta mixture.

Pour into 4 dessert glasses. Refrigerate for 2 to 3 hours, or until set.

In a cup, mix 1 tablespoon of the juice and the cornstarch until smooth.

Place the remaining juice in a small saucepan. Bring to a boil over medium-high heat. Whisk in the cornstarch mixture. Boil for 1 minute, or until clear and thickened. Refrigerate until cold.

To serve, drizzle the sauce over the pudding and sprinkle with the pecans.

Makes 4 servings

Per serving: 171 calories, 10 g protein, 11 g carbohydrates, 10 g fat, 4 g saturated fat, 20 mg cholesterol, 105 mg sodium, 1 g dietary fiber

Exchanges: ½ milk, ½ other carbohydrate, ½ fat

Ginger Pumpkin Pie   *page 112*

Raspberry-Almond Tart *page 122*

Apple Strudel *page 266*

Cappuccino Custard   *page 160*

Raspberry Trifle   *page 161*

Chocolate Pudding Cups   *page 136*

Chocolate-Cinnamon Flans   *page 162*

Chocolate Mousse *page 158*

Apricot Squares   *page 200*

Thumbprint Cookies   *page 182*

Cherry-Oatmeal Cookies
page 185

Lemon Bars   *page 199*

Clockwise from left: Peanut Butter Sandies, *page 183*; Orange-Walnut Biscotti, *page 195*; Chocolate Almond Meringue Cookies, *page 175*

Chocolate Almond Fudge Brownies   *page 201*

Chocolate Chippers   *page 174*

Banana-Mango Mousse

2   *ripe mangoes, peeled and coarsely chopped (about 2½ cups)*

½   *cup (4 ounces) fat-free vanilla yogurt*

1   *small banana*

2   *teaspoons honey*

2   *drops vanilla extract*

3   *ice cubes*

4   *sprigs mint*

In a food processor or blender, combine the mangoes, yogurt, banana, honey, vanilla extract, and ice cubes. Process with on/off turns until the ice is broken up. Process until smooth. Remove any remaining large pieces of ice.

Divide the mixture among 4 dessert dishes. Garnish with the mint. Serve immediately.

Makes 4 servings

Per serving: 128 calories, 2 g protein, 32 g carbohydrates, 1 g fat, 1 g saturated fat, 1 mg cholesterol, 24 mg sodium, 3 g dietary fiber

Exchanges: 1½ fruit, ½ other carbohydrate

Variation

Serve with Chocolate Sauce on page 218.

Chocolate Mousse

Photograph
on page 149

¾   cup 1% milk

1   tablespoon instant coffee powder

⅔   cup unsweetened cocoa powder

¼   cup packed light brown sugar

1   egg

2   tablespoons coffee liqueur
    or strong brewed coffee

1   teaspoon unflavored gelatin

2   ounces bittersweet chocolate, coarsely chopped

1   tablespoon vanilla extract

4   egg whites, at room temperature

½   cup granulated sugar

½   teaspoon cream of tartar

1   cup fat-free whipped topping

In a medium saucepan, mix the milk and coffee powder. Cook over medium heat, stirring occasionally, for 2 to 3 minutes, or until steaming. Whisk in the cocoa powder and brown sugar until smooth.

In a small bowl, lightly beat the egg with a fork. Whisk about ½ cup of the milk mixture into the egg. Gradually whisk the egg mixture into the saucepan.

Reduce the heat to low and cook, whisking constantly, for 5 minutes, or until thickened. Remove from the heat.

Place the coffee liqueur or brewed coffee in a cup. Sprinkle with the gelatin. Let stand for 1 minute to soften. Stir into the cocoa mixture until the gelatin dissolves. Add the chocolate and vanilla extract. Stir until the chocolate is melted.

Pour into a large bowl and let stand for 30 minutes, or until cooled.

Pour about 2" of water into a medium saucepan and bring to a simmer.

In a large heatproof bowl that will fit over the saucepan, whisk together the egg whites, granulated sugar, and cream of tartar. Set the bowl over the simmering water and gently whisk for 2 minutes, or until an instant-read thermometer registers 140°F. (The mixture will be too hot to touch.)

Remove from the heat. Using an electric mixer on medium-high speed, beat for 5 minutes, or until cool.

Fold into the chocolate mixture. Fold in the whipped topping. Divide among 8 dessert glasses and refrigerate for at least 2 hours or up to 24 hours.

Makes 8 servings

Per serving: 165 calories, 5 g protein, 28 g carbohydrates, 4 g fat, 2 g saturated fat, 25 mg cholesterol, 60 mg sodium, 2 g dietary fiber

Exchanges: 2 other carbohydrate, ½ very lean meat, 1 fat

Cappuccino Custard

Photograph
on page 145

½ cup sugar

3 tablespoons cornstarch

1 tablespoon instant espresso powder

2 cups 2% milk

2 egg yolks

1 teaspoon vanilla extract

1 cup fat-free whipped topping

   Ground cinnamon

   Cocoa powder

In a medium saucepan, mix the sugar, cornstarch, and espresso powder. Whisk in the milk. Bring to a boil over medium heat and cook, stirring constantly, for 20 minutes, or until the mixture thickens.

In a small bowl, lightly whisk the egg yolks. Whisk in about 1 cup of the milk mixture. Pour into the saucepan and cook, stirring constantly, for 2 minutes, or until the custard has thickened. Stir in the vanilla extract.

Pour into a bowl and place a piece of plastic wrap on the surface. Refrigerate for 30 minutes.

Fold the whipped topping into the cooled custard. Spoon into 6 dessert cups. Refrigerate for at least 1 hour. To serve, dust with the cinnamon and cocoa powder.

Makes 6 servings

Per serving: 165 calories, 4 g protein, 28 g carbohydrates, 3 g fat, 2 g saturated fat, 77 mg cholesterol, 53 mg sodium, 0 g dietary fiber

Exchanges: ½ starch, ½ milk, 1 other carbohydrate, ½ fat

Raspberry Trifle

1	*package (4-serving-size) fat-free instant chocolate pudding mix*
2	*cups fat-free milk*
1	*package (10 ounces) fat-free marble pound cake, cut into ½" slices*
1	*jar (10 ounces) all-fruit raspberry preserves*
¼	*cup dry sherry or orange juice*
1	*pint strawberries, sliced*

Photograph on page 146

Combine the pudding mix and milk in a large bowl. Whisk for 2 minutes, or until thickened.

Arrange a single layer of the cake slices in the bottom of a deep glass bowl. Spread with one-third of the preserves and sprinkle with a generous tablespoon of sherry or orange juice. Top with one-third of the strawberries and one-third of the pudding.

Repeat the layering 2 more times, ending with the pudding. Cover with plastic wrap and refrigerate for at least 2 hours.

Makes 8 servings

Per serving: 283 calories, 4 g protein, 64 g carbohydrates, 0 g fat, 0 g saturated fat, 0 mg cholesterol, 390 mg sodium, 2 g dietary fiber

Exchanges: 4 other carbohydrate

Baking Tip: A trifle is best if made the day before serving.

Chocolate-Cinnamon Flans

*Photograph
on page 148*

4   cups 1% milk

¼   cup unsweetened cocoa powder

1   teaspoon ground cinnamon

1   cup sugar

3   tablespoons water

4   eggs

1   teaspoon vanilla extract

Preheat the oven to 350°F. Place six 4-ounce custard cups in a baking dish.

In a large saucepan, mix the milk, cocoa powder, cinnamon, and ¼ cup of the sugar. Bring to a boil over medium heat. Cook, stirring often, for 20 to 25 minutes, or until reduced to about 2 cups. Let cool slightly.

In a medium saucepan, mix the water and the remaining ¾ cup sugar. Stir over medium-high heat for 1 minute, or until the sugar is dissolved. Cover, bring to a boil, and cook for 2 to 3 minutes, or until the bubbles are thick.

Uncover, reduce the heat to medium, and cook, without stirring, for 2 minutes, or until the syrup darkens to a medium amber color. Immediately pour the syrup into the custard cups and swirl to coat the bottoms and halfway up the sides.

Whisk the eggs in a large bowl. Slowly whisk in the milk mixture. Whisk in the vanilla extract, then strain the mixture through a sieve and pour into the custard cups.

Fill the baking dish with ½" of warm water and cover with foil. Bake for 30 to 40 minutes, or until the custards are just set.

Remove the pan from the oven and carefully remove the cups from the pan. Let cool on a rack for 15 minutes, then refrigerate for at least 1 hour.

To serve, run a knife around the edge of each cup and invert onto a plate.

Makes 6 servings

Per serving: 258 calories, 10 g protein, 44 g carbohydrates, 6 g fat, 2 g saturated fat, 150 mg cholesterol, 125 mg sodium, 1 g dietary fiber

Exchanges: 1 milk, 2 other carbohydrate, ½ lean meat, ½ fat

Crème Caramel

3	tablespoons water
1¼	cups sugar
2	cups 2% milk
4	eggs
1	teaspoon vanilla extract

Preheat the oven to 350°F. Place six 4-ounce custard cups in a baking dish.

In a medium saucepan, mix the water and ¾ cup of the sugar. Cook over medium-high heat, stirring, for 1 minute, or until the sugar is dissolved. Cover the pan, bring to a boil, and cook for 2 to 3 minutes, or until the bubbles are thick.

Uncover, reduce the heat to medium, and cook, without stirring, for 2 minutes, or until the syrup darkens to a medium amber color. Immediately pour the syrup into the custard cups and swirl to coat the bottoms and halfway up the sides.

In another medium saucepan, mix the milk and the remaining ½ cup sugar. Cook over medium heat, stirring occasionally, until steaming. Remove from the heat.

Whisk the eggs in a large bowl. Slowly whisk in the milk mixture. Whisk in the vanilla extract, then strain the mixture through a sieve and pour into the custard cups.

Fill the baking dish with ½" of warm water and cover with foil. Bake for 30 to 40 minutes, or until the custards are just set.

Remove the pan from the oven and carefully remove the cups from the pan. Let cool on a rack for 15 minutes, then refrigerate for at least 1 hour.

To serve, run a knife around the edge of each cup and invert onto a plate.

Makes 6 servings

Per serving: 261 calories, 8 g protein, 46 g carbohydrates, 5 g fat, 2 g saturated fat, 170 mg cholesterol, 90 mg sodium, 0 g dietary fiber

Exchanges: ½ milk, 2½ other carbohydrate, ½ lean meat, 1 fat

Baking Tip: **What's the difference between flan, crème caramel, and crème brûlée? Flan and crème caramel are simply two different names for a custard that's baked in a dish lined with caramel. Crème brûlée, on the other hand, is a chilled custard that is sprinkled with sugar and then placed under a broiler to create a hard glaze of caramelized sugar.**

Peanut Butter Bread Pudding with Raisins

> 6 slices raisin bread, cut into 1" cubes
> 1¾ cups 1% milk
> 4 eggs
> ¾ cup creamy peanut butter
> 3 tablespoons packed light brown sugar
> 1 teaspoon vanilla extract

Coat a 9" x 9" baking dish with cooking spray.

Place the bread in a baking dish.

In a blender, combine the milk, eggs, peanut butter, brown sugar, and vanilla extract. Process until smooth. Pour evenly over the bread, saturating the cubes. Cover with foil and refrigerate overnight.

Preheat the oven to 350°F.

Remove the foil from the baking dish and bake for 35 minutes, or until lightly browned and puffed. Cool on a rack for 15 minutes. Serve warm or at room temperature.

Makes 12 servings

Per serving: 173 calories, 9 g protein, 12 g carbohydrates, 11 g fat, 2 g saturated fat, 83 mg cholesterol, 168 mg sodium, 2 g dietary fiber

Exchanges: ½ starch, ½ lean meat, 2 fat

Peach Bread Pudding

8   *slices multigrain bread, cut into 1" cubes*

2   *cups 2% milk*

¾   *cup peach all-fruit preserves*

2   *teaspoons vanilla extract*

¾   *teaspoon ground cinnamon*

⅛   *teaspoon salt*

5   *eggs*

¼   *cup dried cranberries, blueberries, or cherries*

Coat a 9" x 9" baking dish with cooking spray.

Place the bread in a baking dish.

In a large saucepan, mix the milk, preserves, vanilla extract, cinnamon, and salt. Cook over medium heat, stirring occasionally, until steaming.

Place the eggs in a large bowl and whisk to combine. Whisk in about ½ cup of the milk mixture until smooth. Then whisk in the remaining milk mixture. Pour evenly over the bread, saturating the cubes. Cover with foil and let stand for 30 minutes.

Preheat the oven to 350°F.

Remove the foil from the baking dish and bake for 45 to 50 minutes, or until a knife inserted in the center comes out clean. Cool on a rack for 15 minutes. Serve warm or at room temperature.

Makes 8 servings

Per serving: 219 calories, 9 g protein, 34 g carbohydrates, 5 g fat, 2 g saturated fat, 135 mg cholesterol, 250 mg sodium, 2 g dietary fiber

Exchanges: 1 starch, 1 other carbohydrate, ½ lean meat, ½ fat

Raspberry Bread Pudding

2   *cups 2% milk*

½   *cup liquid egg substitute*

½   *cup maple syrup*

¼   *cup oat bran*

2   *teaspoons vanilla extract*

¼   *teaspoon ground cinnamon*

5   *cups multigrain bread cubes*

4   *cups raspberries*

1   *tablespoon chilled butter, cut into small pieces*

1   *cup (8 ounces) low-fat vanilla yogurt*

Preheat the oven to 350°F. Coat a 9" x 9" baking dish with cooking spray.

In a large bowl, mix the milk, egg substitute, maple syrup, oat bran, vanilla extract, and cinnamon. Add the bread and stir to coat. Let stand for 10 minutes.

Fold in the raspberries. Place in the prepared baking dish. Sprinkle with the butter.

Bake for 45 minutes, or until a knife inserted in the center comes out clean. Cool on a rack for 15 minutes. Serve warm or cold, topped with the yogurt.

Makes 8 servings

Per serving: 215 calories, 8 g protein, 37 g carbohydrates, 5 g fat, 2 g saturated fat, 10 mg cholesterol, 173 mg sodium, 6 g dietary fiber

Exchanges: ½ starch, ½ fruit, ½ milk, 1 other carbohydrate, 1 very lean meat, 1 fat

Warm Gingerbread-Pumpkin Pudding

2	eggs
2	egg whites
¼	cup molasses
¼	cup granulated sugar
1	cup canned pumpkin
¾	cup fat-free milk
⅓	cup whole grain pastry flour
2	teaspoons ground ginger
1½	teaspoons ground cinnamon
1	teaspoon baking powder
½	teaspoon baking soda
¼	teaspoon ground allspice
1	teaspoon confectioners' sugar

Preheat the oven to 400°F. Coat a 9" x 9" baking dish with cooking spray.

In a large bowl, mix the eggs, egg whites, molasses, and granulated sugar. Stir in the pumpkin, milk, flour, ginger, cinnamon, baking powder, baking soda, and allspice. Pour into the prepared baking dish.

Bake for 25 minutes, or until the pudding is lightly browned and cracked around the edges but still a bit soft in the center. Cool on a rack for 10 minutes.

Just before serving, place the confectioners' sugar in a small sieve and dust over the warm pudding.

Makes 6 servings

Per serving: 178 calories, 6 g protein, 35 g carbohydrates, 2 g fat, 1 g saturated fat, 70 mg cholesterol, 300 mg sodium, 2 g dietary fiber

Exchanges: ½ starch, 1½ other carbohydrate, ½ lean meat

Coconut-Raisin Bread Pudding

1½	cups 2% milk
1	cup fat-free evaporated milk
4	cups dry whole wheat bread or raisin bread, cut into 1" pieces
2	eggs
½	cup sugar
½	teaspoon salt
½	teaspoon vanilla extract
½	cup packed, unsweetened coconut
½	cup raisins

Coat a slow cooker with cooking spray. In a medium bowl, combine the milk, evaporated milk, and bread pieces. Stir thoroughly to mix.

Using an electric mixer on medium speed, beat the eggs, sugar, salt, and vanilla extract. Add to the bread and milk mixture in the slow cooker.

Stir in the coconut and raisins. Cover. Cook on high for 3 hours. Serve warm or chilled.

Makes 8 servings

Per serving: 243 calories, 9 g protein, 41 g carbohydrates, 6 g fat, 4 g saturated fat, 58 mg cholesterol, 381 mg sodium, 3 g dietary fiber

Exchanges: 1 starch, ½ milk, ½ fruit, ½ other carbohydrate, 1 fat

Baking Tip: This is a tasty way to use stale or leftover bread. And save some coconut for puddin' on your pudding.

Chocolate Bread Pudding

4   cups cubed day-old bread, such as white, raisin, sourdough,
    or oatmeal

2   cups fat-free milk, scalded (See Baking Tip below)

¼   cup unsweetened Dutch processed or European-style cocoa, sifted

¾   cup fat-free liquid egg substitute

¾   cup packed dark brown sugar

1   teaspoon vanilla extract

1   teaspoon brandy or rum (optional)
    Confectioners' sugar (optional)

Preheat the oven to 350°F. Coat a 2-quart baking dish with cooking spray.

Place the bread cubes in the prepared baking dish and set aside.

In a medium bowl, stir together the milk and cocoa until the cocoa is dissolved. Stir in the egg substitute, brown sugar, vanilla extract, and brandy or rum (if using).

Pour the milk mixture over the bread. Bake for 35 to 40 minutes, or until set. Cool on a wire rack for 10 minutes. Lightly dust the top with confectioners' sugar (if using). Serve warm.

Makes 8 servings

Per serving: 180 calories, 7 g protein, 34 g carbohydrates, 4 g fat, 0 g saturated fat, 2 mg cholesterol, 201 mg sodium, 1 g dietary fiber

Exchanges: ½ starch, 1½ other carbohydrate, ½ very lean meat

Baking Tip: Before scalding milk, rinse the pan with cold water. Then add the milk and heat it over medium heat. When bubbles begin to form around the sides of the pan, take it off the heat. Don't allow the milk to boil.

Italian Parfaits

½   *cup boiling water*

2   *teaspoons instant espresso powder*

8   *chocolate chip biscotti, crushed*

2⅔ *cups fat-free vanilla frozen yogurt*

4   *teaspoons grated semisweet chocolate*

In a small bowl, mix the water and espresso powder. Let cool.

Divide one-third of the biscotti crumbs among 4 parfait glasses. In each glass, layer ⅓ cup of the frozen yogurt, 1 tablespoon of the espresso, and ½ teaspoon of the chocolate. Repeat, starting with biscotti crumbs.

Top with the remaining biscotti crumbs. Serve immediately or freeze for up to 1 hour.

Makes 4 servings

Per serving: 387 calories, 9 g protein, 58 g carbohydrates, 13 g fat, 7 g saturated fat, 42 mg cholesterol, 149 mg sodium, 4 g dietary fiber

Exchanges: 4 other carbohydrate, 2½ fat

Baking Tips: Biscotti are crunchy Italian cookies often made with very little fat. They can be purchased in most supermarkets and in Italian food stores.

To crush the biscotti, place them in a heavy-duty plastic bag, seal, and tap with a rolling pin. Create your own version of this recipe by using different flavors of fat-free frozen yogurt and biscotti.

Orange Gelatin Whip

2   packages (4-serving-size) sugar-free orange gelatin

2   cups boiling water

1   cup cold water

⅓   cup reduced-fat sour cream

⅓   cup part-skim ricotta cheese

⅓   cup reduced-fat cream cheese

½   teaspoon vanilla extract

Place the gelatin in a large bowl and whisk in the boiling water until the gelatin is dissolved. Whisk in the cold water. Cover and refrigerate for 2 hours, or until firm.

In a blender, combine the sour cream, ricotta, cream cheese, and vanilla extract. Blend on high speed until light and fluffy. Cut the gelatin into blocks and spoon into the blender. Blend for 3 to 4 minutes, or until smooth and frothy. Pour into 6 dessert dishes. Cover and refrigerate for at least 1 hour.

Makes 6 servings

Per serving: 179 calories, 32 g protein, 3 g carbohydrates, 5 g fat, 3 g saturated fat, 15 mg cholesterol, 130 mg sodium, 0 g dietary fiber

Exchanges: ½ lean meat, 3 very lean meat, 1 fat

Cookies *and* Bars

Found in almost every shape, size, and variety, cookies appeal to virtually everyone. Easy to make and fun to eat, these "little cakes," as the word translates from the Dutch word *koekje*, make a great snack to gobble on the go or to enjoy leisurely with a tall glass of milk. As you will see, these classic recipes have been made healthier by using whole grain pastry flour and cocoa powder instead of white flour and full-fat chocolate. Substituting reduced-fat or fat-free cream cheese for some of the butter further cuts the fat but still creates rich cookies for you to enjoy.

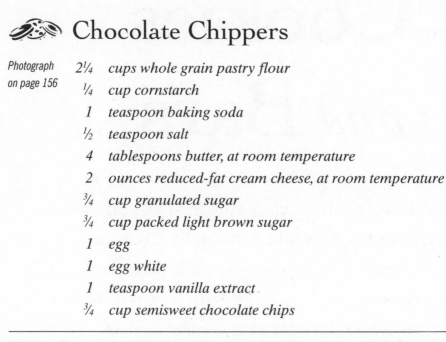

Chocolate Chippers

Photograph on page 156

2¼	cups whole grain pastry flour
¼	cup cornstarch
1	teaspoon baking soda
½	teaspoon salt
4	tablespoons butter, at room temperature
2	ounces reduced-fat cream cheese, at room temperature
¾	cup granulated sugar
¾	cup packed light brown sugar
1	egg
1	egg white
1	teaspoon vanilla extract
¾	cup semisweet chocolate chips

Preheat the oven to 375°F. Coat 2 large baking sheets with cooking spray.

In a medium bowl, mix the flour, cornstarch, baking soda, and salt.

Place the butter and cream cheese in a large bowl. Using an electric mixer on medium speed, beat for 1 minute, or until smooth. Beat in the granulated sugar and brown sugar until light and creamy. Beat in the egg, egg white, and vanilla extract.

Reduce the mixer speed to low. Add the flour mixture in 2 batches, beating just until combined. Stir in the chocolate chips. Drop the dough by rounded teaspoons about 1½" apart onto the prepared baking sheets.

Bake 1 sheet at a time for 9 to 12 minutes, or until golden. Cool on a rack for 2 minutes. Remove from the sheet and place on the rack to cool completely.

Makes 40

Per cookie: 67 calories, 1 g protein, 10 g carbohydrates, 3 g fat, 1 g saturated fat, 10 mg cholesterol, 80 mg sodium, 1 g dietary fiber

Exchanges: ½ starch, ½ other carbohydrate, ½ fat

Chocolate Almond Meringue Cookies

*Photograph
on page 154*

½   cup blanched almonds

5   tablespoons sugar

3   egg whites, at room temperature

¼   teaspoon cream of tartar

2   tablespoons unsweetened cocoa powder

¼   cup raspberry or strawberry all-fruit preserves

Preheat the oven to 250°F. Line a baking sheet with parchment paper or foil.

Place the almonds and 2 tablespoons of the sugar in a food processor. Process until finely ground.

Place the egg whites and cream of tartar in a large bowl. Using an electric mixer on high speed, beat until frothy. Gradually add the remaining 3 tablespoons sugar and beat until stiff, glossy peaks form. Gently fold in the cocoa powder and ground almonds.

Spoon the meringue into 1½" mounds on the prepared baking sheet. Using the back of a spoon, depress the centers and build up the sides of each meringue to form a shallow cup.

Bake for 1 hour. Turn off the oven and allow the meringues to stand with the oven door closed for 1 hour. Remove from the sheet and place on a rack to cool completely.

Store in an airtight container. To serve, fill each meringue with ¼ teaspoon of the preserves.

Makes 16

Per cookie: 61 calories, 2 g protein, 9 g carbohydrates, 2 g fat, 1 g saturated fat, 0 mg cholesterol, 10 mg sodium, 1 g dietary fiber

Exchanges: ½ other carbohydrate, ½ fat

Triple Chocolate Drops

1¾   cups whole grain pastry flour

½   cup unsweetened cocoa powder

1   teaspoon baking powder

½   teaspoon baking soda

¼   teaspoon salt

1   ounce unsweetened chocolate

3   tablespoons canola oil

4   egg whites

1   egg

¾   cup granulated sugar

½   cup packed light brown sugar

¼   cup prune puree

1   teaspoon vanilla extract

¼   cup miniature semisweet chocolate chips

    Confectioners' sugar (optional)

In a medium bowl, mix the flour, cocoa powder, baking powder, baking soda, and salt.

Place the chocolate and oil in a small microwaveable bowl. Microwave on high power for 1 minute. Stir until the chocolate is melted and smooth.

In a large bowl, combine the egg whites, egg, granulated sugar, and brown sugar. Using an electric mixer on high speed, beat for 3 to 5 minutes, or until smooth and pale. Reduce the speed to low and add the melted chocolate, prune puree, and vanilla extract. Beat for 1 minute.

Gradually beat in the flour mixture. Fold in the chocolate chips. Cover and refrigerate for 1 hour or up to 24 hours.

Preheat the oven to 350°F. Coat 2 large baking sheets with cooking spray.

Let the dough soften at room temperature for 5 to 10 minutes. Drop by rounded teaspoons about 1½" apart onto the prepared baking sheets.

Bake 1 sheet at a time for 12 minutes, or until the centers just begin to set. Cool on a rack for 2 minutes. Remove from the sheet and place on the rack to cool completely. Lightly dust with the confectioners' sugar (if using).

Makes 36

Per cookie: 64 calories, 2 g protein, 11 g carbohydrates, 2 g fat, 1 g saturated fat, 9 mg cholesterol, 55 mg sodium, 1 g dietary fiber

Exchanges: ½ starch, ½ other carbohydrate, ½ fat

Baking Tip: Prune puree is a great fat replacer in chocolate baked goods as long as you don't use too much. Substitute the puree for up to two-thirds of the fat.

To make your own, combine 12 ounces pitted prunes and 3 tablespoons corn syrup in a food processor. Process for 10 seconds. Add ½ cup water and process until smooth. Refrigerate in an airtight container for up to 2 months.

Alternatives to homemade prune puree include pureed baby food prunes, lekvar, and commercial fat substitutes made with prunes and sweeteners such as corn syrup. These products are not quite as thick and flavorful as homemade prune puree, but they are adequate substitutes.

Mocha Meringue Kisses

2   tablespoons unsweetened cocoa powder

1   tablespoon whole grain pastry flour

½   teaspoon instant coffee powder

2   egg whites, at room temperature

⅛   teaspoon salt

½   cup sugar

Preheat the oven to 225°F. Line 2 large baking sheets with parchment paper or foil.

In a small bowl, mix the cocoa powder, flour, and coffee powder.

Place the egg whites and salt in a large bowl. Using an electric mixer on medium speed, beat until foamy. On high speed, gradually beat in the sugar until stiff, glossy peaks form. Fold in the cocoa mixture just until blended.

Drop the meringue by rounded teaspoons about 1" apart onto the prepared baking sheets.

Bake for 1 hour. Turn off the oven and allow the meringues to stand with the oven door closed for 1 hour. Remove from the sheets and place on a rack to cool completely.

Makes 42

Per cookie: 11 calories, 0 g protein, 3 g carbohydrates, 0 g fat, 0 g saturated fat, 0 mg cholesterol, 12 mg sodium, 0 g dietary fiber

Exchanges: 0

Apricot Kisses

6	tablespoons butter, at room temperature
½	cup granulated sugar
¾	cup apricot all-fruit preserves
1	egg
1	teaspoon grated orange rind
¼	teaspoon almond extract
1¾	cups whole grain pastry flour
2	tablespoons cornstarch
½	teaspoon baking powder
¼	teaspoon salt
¼	cup confectioners' sugar

Preheat the oven to 375°F. Coat 2 large baking sheets with cooking spray.

Place the butter in a large bowl. Using an electric mixer on medium speed, beat until light and fluffy. Add the granulated sugar and ¼ cup of the preserves. Beat until well blended. Add the egg, orange rind, and almond extract. Beat for 2 minutes.

In a medium bowl, mix the flour, cornstarch, baking powder, and salt. Gradually add to the apricot mixture and beat on low speed just until incorporated. Refrigerate the dough for 10 minutes, or until slightly firm.

Form the dough into 1" balls. Place on the prepared baking sheets, leaving 1½" between balls. Dip the back of a ¼-teaspoon measuring spoon into the confectioners' sugar and press a deep indentation in the center of each ball. Fill the indentation with ¼ to ½ teaspoon of the remaining preserves.

Bake 1 sheet at a time for 10 minutes, or until the cookies are just tinged with brown. Cool on a rack for 2 minutes. Remove from the sheet and place on the rack to cool completely.

Makes 36

Per cookie: 60 calories, 1 g protein, 10 g carbohydrates, 2 g fat, 0 g saturated fat, 5 mg cholesterol, 25 mg sodium, 1 g dietary fiber

Exchanges: ½ other carbohydrate, ½ fat

Baking Tip: These cookies can be stored in an airtight container for up to 1 week or frozen for up to 1 month.

Crunchy Peanut Butter Cookies

¾   cup packed light brown sugar

¼   cup granulated sugar

5   tablespoons butter

¼   cup crunchy peanut butter

1   teaspoon vanilla extract

1   egg white

3   tablespoons water

1¾   cups unbleached flour

¾   teaspoon baking soda

¼   teaspoon salt

Preheat the oven to 350°F. Coat 2 large baking sheets with cooking spray or line with parchment paper.

In a medium bowl, cream together the brown sugar, granulated sugar, butter, and peanut butter until smooth. Add the vanilla extract, egg white, and water. Using an electric mixer on medium speed, beat until light.

In another medium bowl, combine the flour, baking soda, and salt. Stir the flour mixture into the peanut-butter mixture.

Shape the batter into 1" balls and place on the prepared baking sheets, leaving 2" between cookies. Using a fork that has been dipped in water, flatten the cookies. Bake 1 sheet at a time for 10 to 12 minutes, or just until the cookies are set. Cool on a rack for 2 minutes. Remove from the sheet and place on the rack to cool.

Makes 30

Per cookie: 85 calories, 1 g protein, 13 g carbohydrates, 3 g fat, 1 g saturated fat, 0 mg cholesterol, 65 mg sodium, 0 g dietary fiber

Exchanges: ½ starch, ½ other carbohydrate, ½ fat

Spiced Molasses Cookies

2	cups whole grain pastry flour
2	teaspoons ground cinnamon
2	teaspoons ground ginger
1	teaspoon baking soda
½	teaspoon ground cloves
½	teaspoon salt
1	cup sugar
¼	cup unsweetened applesauce
¼	cup canola oil
¼	cup molasses
2	egg whites

Preheat the oven to 350°F. Coat 2 large baking sheets with cooking spray.

In a medium bowl, mix the flour, cinnamon, ginger, baking soda, cloves, and salt.

In a large bowl, combine the sugar, applesauce, oil, molasses, and egg whites. Using an electric mixer on medium speed, beat for 1 minute, or until well combined. With the mixer at low speed, gradually beat in the flour mixture.

Drop the dough by level tablespoons about 1" apart onto the prepared baking sheets.

Bake 1 sheet at a time for 10 minutes, or until lightly browned. Cool on a rack for 2 minutes. Remove from the sheet and place on the rack to cool completely.

Makes 42

Per cookie: 52 calories, 1 g protein, 10 g carbohydrates, 1 g fat, 0 g saturated fat, 0 mg cholesterol, 60 mg sodium, 1 g dietary fiber

Exchanges: ½ starch, ½ other carbohydrate, ½ fat

Baking Tip: When trying this recipe for the first time, check the oven after about 8 minutes to see whether the cookies are done. Baked goods with molasses have a tendency to overbrown, so the baking time may be shorter than what's suggested.

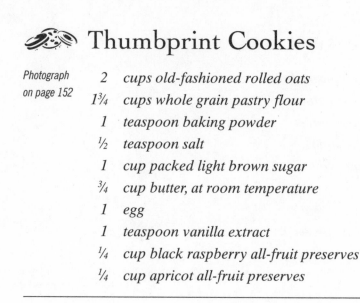 # Thumbprint Cookies

Photograph on page 152

2	cups old-fashioned rolled oats
1¾	cups whole grain pastry flour
1	teaspoon baking powder
½	teaspoon salt
1	cup packed light brown sugar
¾	cup butter, at room temperature
1	egg
1	teaspoon vanilla extract
¼	cup black raspberry all-fruit preserves
¼	cup apricot all-fruit preserves

Preheat the oven to 350°F. Coat 2 large baking sheets with cooking spray.

In a medium bowl, mix the oats, flour, baking powder, and salt.

Place the brown sugar and butter in a large bowl. Using an electric mixer on medium speed, beat for 3 minutes, or until light and fluffy. Beat in the egg and vanilla extract. Gradually beat in the flour mixture.

Shape the dough into 1" balls and place on the prepared baking sheets, leaving 2" between balls. Dip your thumb into water and make an indentation in the center of each cookie. Spoon ½ teaspoon of the raspberry preserves into the centers of half of the cookies. Fill the remaining cookies with the apricot preserves.

Bake 1 sheet at a time for 12 minutes, or until lightly browned and firm to the touch. Cool on a rack for 2 minutes. Remove from the sheet and place on the rack to cool completely.

Makes 45

Per cookie: 80 calories, 1 g protein, 12 g carbohydrates, 3 g fat, 2 g saturated fat, 15 mg cholesterol, 70 mg sodium, 1 g dietary fiber

Exchanges: ½ starch, ½ other carbohydrate, ½ fat

Peanut Butter Sandies

*Photograph
on page 154*

1¾	cups whole grain pastry flour
½	cup confectioners' sugar
2	tablespoons cornstarch
1½	teaspoons baking powder
½	teaspoon baking soda
¼	teaspoon salt
½	cup packed light brown sugar
⅓	cup chunky peanut butter
¼	cup canola oil
1	egg
2	teaspoons vanilla extract

Preheat the oven to 375°F. Coat 2 large baking sheets with cooking spray.

In a medium bowl, mix the flour, confectioners' sugar, cornstarch, baking powder, baking soda, and salt.

In a large bowl, combine the brown sugar, peanut butter, and oil. Using an electric mixer on medium speed, beat until well combined. Beat in the egg and vanilla extract. Stir in the flour mixture. (The dough will be crumbly.)

Form the dough into 1" balls and place on the prepared baking sheets, leaving 2" between balls. Flatten the balls with the bottom of a glass.

Bake 1 sheet at a time for 7 to 8 minutes, or until lightly browned. Cool on a rack for 2 minutes. Remove from the sheet and place on the rack to cool completely.

Makes 40
Per cookie: 37 calories, 1 g protein, 6 g carbohydrates, 1 g fat, 0 g saturated fat, 5 mg cholesterol, 60 mg sodium, 1 g dietary fiber
Exchanges: ½ starch

Oatmeal Cookies with Cranberries and Chocolate Chips

2	cups old-fashioned rolled oats
½	cup whole grain pastry flour
¾	teaspoon baking soda
½	teaspoon ground cinnamon
¼	teaspoon salt
½	cup packed light brown sugar
⅓	cup canola oil
3	egg whites
2	teaspoons vanilla extract
¾	cup dried cranberries
½	cup miniature semisweet chocolate chips

Preheat the oven to 350°F. Coat 2 large baking sheets with cooking spray.

In a large bowl, mix the oats, flour, baking soda, cinnamon, and salt.

In a medium bowl, mix the brown sugar, oil, egg whites, and vanilla extract until smooth. Stir in the cranberries and chocolate chips. Add to the flour mixture and stir just until blended.

Drop the dough by scant tablespoons about 1½" apart onto the prepared baking sheets.

Bake 1 sheet at a time for 10 minutes, or until golden brown. Cool on a rack for 2 minutes. Remove from the sheet and place on the rack to cool completely.

Makes 18

Per cookie: 144 calories, 3 g protein, 20 g carbohydrates, 6 g fat, 1 g saturated fat, 0 mg cholesterol, 95 mg sodium, 2 g dietary fiber

Exchanges: ½ starch, ½ fruit, ½ other carbohydrate, 1 fat

Cherry-Oatmeal Cookies

Photograph on page 152

3	cups old-fashioned rolled oats
1½	cups whole grain pastry flour
1	teaspoon ground cinnamon
¼	teaspoon ground cardamom
½	teaspoon baking soda
¼	teaspoon salt
¾	cup butter, at room temperature
¼	cup reduced-fat cream cheese, at room temperature
¾	cup packed light brown sugar
¾	cup granulated sugar
2	eggs
½	teaspoon almond extract
2	cups dried cherries, chopped

Preheat the oven to 350°F.

In a medium bowl, mix the oats, flour, cinnamon, cardamom, baking soda, and salt.

In a large bowl, combine the butter, cream cheese, brown sugar, and granulated sugar. Using an electric mixer on medium speed, beat for 3 minutes, or until light and fluffy. Beat in the eggs and almond extract. Gradually beat in the oat mixture. Stir in the cherries.

Drop by rounded tablespoons about 2" apart onto 2 ungreased baking sheets.

Bake 1 sheet at a time for 10 minutes, or until golden brown. Cool on a rack for 2 minutes. Remove from the sheet and place on the rack to cool completely.

Makes 48

Per cookie: 104 calories, 2 g protein, 16 g carbohydrates, 4 g fat, 2 g saturated fat, 15 mg cholesterol, 65 mg sodium, 1 g dietary fiber

Exchanges: ½ starch, ½ other carbohydrate, ½ fat

Oatmeal-Pecan Lace Cookies

1	cup old-fashioned rolled oats
½	cup packed light brown sugar
½	cup granulated sugar
¼	cup pecans, toasted and chopped
2	tablespoons whole grain pastry flour
2	tablespoons water
2	tablespoons butter, melted
1	tablespoon canola oil
2	egg whites
1	teaspoon vanilla extract
1	ounce semisweet chocolate, chopped

Preheat the oven to 350°F. Coat 2 large baking sheets with cooking spray.

In a large bowl, mix the oats, brown sugar, granulated sugar, pecans, and flour. Add the water, butter, oil, egg whites, and vanilla extract. Stir to combine.

For each cookie, spoon 2 level teaspoons of the batter onto a baking sheet and smooth it into a 2½" circle. Leaving 1½" between cookies, repeat to make 9 cookies per sheet.

Place both baking sheets in the oven. Bake for 7 minutes (switch the sheets after 3 minutes), or until the edges are lightly browned. Cool on racks for 2 minutes. Remove from the sheets and place on the racks to cool completely.

Repeat to use the remaining batter and make a total of 36 cookies.

When the cookies have cooled completely, transfer them back to the baking sheets.

Melt the chocolate in a small saucepan over low heat. Transfer to a small plastic food storage bag. With scissors, snip a small piece from the corner of the bag. Drizzle some melted chocolate over each cookie. Freeze the cookies for 5 minutes, or until the chocolate hardens.

Makes 36

Per cookie: 42 calories, 1 g protein, 6 g carbohydrates, 2 g fat, 1 g saturated fat, 0 mg cholesterol, 10 mg sodium, 0 g dietary fiber

Exchanges: ½ fat

Baking Tip: These lacy cookies can also be formed into tuiles, which are curve-shaped cookies so named because they resemble French roof tiles. To make, place the still-warm cookies over a slender rolling pin to shape them. Remove the cookies from the rolling pin as soon as they are cool and firm.

Lace Cookie Cups with Sorbet

⅓ cup packed light brown sugar

¼ cup light corn syrup

4 tablespoons butter

½ cup whole grain pastry flour

¼ cup finely chopped almonds

⅛ teaspoon salt

Raspberry or other flavor sorbet

Preheat the oven to 375°F. Coat 2 large baking sheets with cooking spray. Invert six 6-ounce custard cups on a work surface.

In a medium saucepan, combine the brown sugar, corn syrup, and butter. Stir over medium heat until the mixture comes to a boil and the sugar dissolves. Remove from the heat.

Stir in the flour, almonds, and salt.

For each cookie, spoon 3 heaping teaspoons of the batter onto a baking sheet and smooth it into a circle. Leaving 3" between cookies, repeat to make 3 cookies per sheet.

Place both baking sheets in the oven. Bake for 4 minutes, or until browned. Cool on racks for 1 minute. Working quickly, use a metal spatula to remove the cookies from the sheets and drape over the upside-down custard cups. Let harden for about 3 minutes.

Repeat with the remaining batter to make a total of 18 cookies.

To serve, spoon sorbet into the cookie cups.

Makes 18

Per cookie cup: 71 calories, 1 g protein, 10 g carbohydrates, 4 g fat, 2 g saturated fat, 7 mg cholesterol, 56 mg sodium, 1 g dietary fiber

Exchanges: ½ other carbohydrate, 1 fat

Apple Pinwheel Cookies

1	cup chopped dried apples
¾	cup apple juice
1	tablespoon lemon juice
½	teaspoon ground cinnamon
2½	cups whole grain pastry flour
1	teaspoon baking powder
¼	teaspoon salt
8	tablespoons butter, at room temperature
¼	cup reduced-fat cream cheese, at room temperature
1	cup sugar
2	eggs
1	teaspoon lemon extract

In a medium saucepan, combine the apples, apple juice, lemon juice, and cinnamon. Bring to a boil over medium-high heat. Reduce the heat to low, cover, and simmer for 35 minutes, or until the apples are tender and most of the juice has been absorbed. Let cool slightly. Mash with a fork.

In a medium bowl, mix the flour, baking powder, and salt.

In a large bowl, combine the butter, cream cheese, and sugar. Using an electric mixer on medium speed, beat for 3 minutes, or until light and fluffy. Beat in the eggs and lemon extract. Gradually beat in the flour mixture. Cover and refrigerate for at least 1 hour.

Divide the dough in half. On a floured surface, roll each half into an 11" x 7" rectangle. Spread half of the apple mixture over each rectangle. Starting at a long side, roll up tightly. Pinch to seal. Wrap in plastic wrap and refrigerate for at least 4 hours, or until firm.

Preheat the oven to 375°F.

Cut the rolls into ½"-thick slices. Place, cut side down, on ungreased baking sheets, leaving about ½" between slices.

Bake 1 sheet at a time for 10 minutes, or until light brown. Cool on a rack for 2 minutes. Remove from the sheet and place on the rack to cool completely.

Makes 44

Per cookie: 66 calories, 1 g protein, 10 g carbohydrates, 3 g fat, 1 g saturated fat, 16 mg cholesterol, 56 mg sodium, 1 g dietary fiber

Exchanges: ½ starch, ½ fat

Fruit and Nut Pinwheels

⅔   cup golden raisins

½   cup + 2 tablespoons raspberry all-fruit preserves

3   tablespoons slivered almonds

4   tablespoons sugar

1   teaspoon ground cinnamon

1   cup whole grain pastry flour

½   cup reduced-fat cream cheese, at room temperature

1   tablespoon butter, at room temperature

Preheat the oven to 350°F. Coat 2 large baking sheets with cooking spray.

In a small bowl, mix the raisins, preserves, and almonds.

In a cup, mix 2 tablespoons of the sugar and the cinnamon. Set both aside.

In a large bowl, combine the flour, cream cheese, butter, and the remaining 2 tablespoons sugar. Using an electric mixer on medium speed, beat well. Divide the dough in half.

Sprinkle half of the sugar mixture on a work surface. Place half of the dough on top. Roll into an 11" x 7" rectangle. Spread half of the raisin mixture over the surface. Starting at a long side, roll up tightly. Pinch to seal. Repeat to use the remaining sugar mixture, dough, and filling.

Cut the rolls into ½"-thick slices. Place, cut side down, on the prepared baking sheets, leaving about ½" between slices.

Bake 1 sheet at a time for 12 to 14 minutes, or until golden. Cool on a rack for 2 minutes. Remove from the sheet and place on the rack to cool completely.

Makes 44

Per cookie: 33 calories, 1 g protein, 7 g carbohydrates, 1 g fat, 0 g saturated fat, 1 mg cholesterol, 4 mg sodium, 0 g dietary fiber

Exchanges: ½ other carbohydrate

Lemon Drop Cookies

> 1   cup + 2 tablespoons whole grain pastry flour
> ⅛   teaspoon baking soda
> ⅛   teaspoon salt
> ½   cup sugar
> 4   tablespoons butter, at room temperature
> 1   large egg white
> 1   teaspoon grated lemon rind
> 1   tablespoon lemon juice

Preheat the oven to 350°F. Coat 2 large baking sheets with cooking spray.

In a medium bowl, mix the flour, baking soda, and salt.

Place the sugar and butter in a large bowl. Using an electric mixer on medium speed, beat until light and fluffy. Add the egg white, lemon rind, and lemon juice. Beat well. (The mixture will appear curdled.)

With the mixer on low speed, gradually beat in the flour mixture.

Drop the dough by rounded teaspoons, about 1" apart, onto the prepared baking sheets.

Bake 1 sheet at a time for 8 to 10 minutes, or until the edges are lightly browned. Cool on a rack for 2 minutes. Remove from the sheet and place on the rack to cool completely.

Makes 36

Per cookie: 29 calories, 1 g protein, 5 g carbohydrates, 1 g fat, 0 g saturated fat, 0 mg cholesterol, 30 mg sodium, 0 g dietary fiber

Exchanges: ½ other carbohydrate, ½ fat

Linzer Cookies

¼   cup trans-free margarine or butter, softened

1   tablespoon canola oil

¾   cup granulated sugar

    Grated rind of l lemon (optional)

1   egg

1   teaspoon vanilla extract

1⅔ cups unbleached flour

1   teaspoon baking powder

¼   teaspoon salt

¼   cup sliced almonds (optional)

⅓   cup raspberry jam

    Confectioners' sugar

In a medium bowl, using an electric mixer on medium speed, beat the margarine, oil, granulated sugar, and lemon rind (if using) until light. Beat in the egg and vanilla extract until smooth.

In a separate bowl, combine the flour, baking powder, and salt. Add the flour mixture to the sugar mixture and stir by hand just until the dough is soft. Divide the dough in half, shape each half into a disk, wrap in plastic, and refrigerate 1 hour, or until well chilled.

When ready to bake, preheat the oven to 350°F. Coat a baking sheet with cooking spray.

Between 2 pieces of waxed paper, roll out 1 disk to ¼" thickness. Cut out cookies using a 1½"- to 2"-round cookie cutter or glass rim. Using a ½"-round or shaped cutter, cut centers out of half the cookies.

Place the cookies 2" to 3" apart on the prepared baking sheet. Sprinkle the cookies with the centers cut out with the almonds (if using), pressing gently to help them adhere.

Bake for 10 to 12 minutes, until lightly golden around edges. Remove from the sheet and place on a rack to cool completely. Repeat with the remaining disk, rerolling scraps once to get as many cookies as possible.

Spread the solid cookies with the jam and sprinkle the cut-out cookies lightly with the confectioners' sugar. Top each solid cookie with a cut-out cookie.

Makes 30

Per cookie: 69 calories, 1 g protein, 12 g carbohydrates, 2 g fat, 0 g saturated fat, 7 mg cholesterol, 50 mg sodium, 0 g dietary fiber

Exchanges: ½ starch, ½ other carbohydrate

Baking Tip: Store these cookies in airtight containers, or freeze them if they aren't going to be eaten within a day or two. Freezing is a good idea for these cookies because they're so low in fat that they don't keep as long as traditional high-fat cookies. Don't store soft and crisp cookies together. The crisp ones will go soggy, and the soft ones will lose moisture.

Lemon-Almond Biscotti

3	cups whole grain pastry flour
½	cup cornmeal
2	teaspoons baking powder
1	egg
2	egg whites
½	cup honey
2	tablespoons canola oil
1	teaspoon almond extract
½	cup lemon juice

Preheat the oven to 350°F. Line a baking sheet with parchment paper or foil.

In a medium bowl, mix the flour, cornmeal, and baking powder.

In a large bowl, mix the egg, egg whites, honey, oil, and almond extract. Stir in the flour mixture. Stir in enough of the lemon juice to form a pliable dough.

Divide the dough in half and form each half into a 12" log.

Place the logs 5" apart on the baking sheet. Slightly flatten each log to ½" high.

Bake for 25 to 30 minutes, or until the tops are firm to the touch. Remove from the oven and let cool on a rack for 3 minutes.

Using a serrated knife, cut each log diagonally into ½"-thick slices. Place the slices, cut side down, on the baking sheet.

Bake for 15 to 20 minutes, or until golden brown; turn the slices halfway through baking. Cool on a rack for 2 minutes. Remove from the sheet and place on the rack to cool completely.

Makes 48

Per biscotti: 43 calories, 1 g protein, 8 g carbohydrates, 1 g fat, 0 g saturated fat, 4 mg cholesterol, 25 mg sodium, 1 g dietary fiber

Exchanges: ½ starch

Orange-Walnut Biscotti

Photograph
on page 154

⅔   cup walnuts

8   tablespoons sugar

1¼   cups whole grain pastry flour

¼   cup cornmeal

1   teaspoon baking powder

¼   teaspoon salt

4   tablespoons butter, at room temperature

2   eggs

2   teaspoons grated orange rind

½   teaspoon orange extract

In a food processor, combine the walnuts and 2 tablespoons of the sugar. Pulse until the walnuts are coarsely ground but not made into a paste. Place in a large bowl and stir in the flour, cornmeal, baking powder, and salt.

Place the butter and the remaining 6 tablespoons sugar in a large bowl. Using an electric mixer on medium speed, beat until light and fluffy. Beat in the eggs, orange rind, and orange extract. Gradually beat in the flour mixture until smooth and thick. Cover and refrigerate for 30 minutes, or until firm.

Preheat the oven to 350°F. Line a baking sheet with parchment paper or foil.

Divide the dough in half and form each half into a 12" log.

Place the logs 5" apart on the baking sheet. Slightly flatten each log to ½" high.

Bake for 25 to 30 minutes, or until the tops are firm to the touch. Remove from the oven and let cool on a rack for 3 minutes.

Using a serrated knife, cut each log diagonally into ½"-thick slices. Place the slices, cut side down, on the baking sheet.

Bake for 10 to 15 minutes, or until golden brown; turn the slices halfway through baking. Cool on a rack for 2 minutes. Remove from the sheet and place on the rack to cool completely.

Makes 48

Per biscotti: 41 calories, 1 g protein, 5 g carbohydrates, 2 g fat, 1 g saturated fat, 11 mg cholesterol, 33 mg sodium

Exchanges: ½ starch, ½ fat

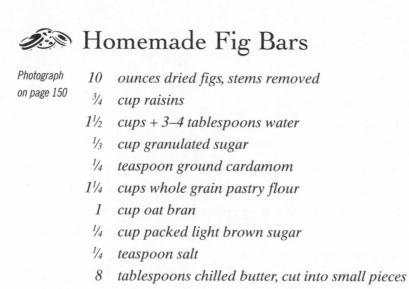

Homemade Fig Bars

Photograph
on page 150

10	ounces dried figs, stems removed
¾	cup raisins
1½	cups + 3–4 tablespoons water
⅓	cup granulated sugar
¼	teaspoon ground cardamom
1¼	cups whole grain pastry flour
1	cup oat bran
¼	cup packed light brown sugar
¼	teaspoon salt
8	tablespoons chilled butter, cut into small pieces

Preheat the oven to 400°F. Coat 2 large baking sheets with cooking spray.

Coarsely chop the figs and place in a food processor. Add the raisins and pulse until fairly smooth. Place in a medium saucepan. Add 1½ cups of the water, the granulated sugar, and cardamom. Bring to a boil over medium-high heat. Reduce the heat to medium-low and cook, stirring occasionally, for 15 minutes, or until the mixture thickens. Remove from the heat.

In a food processor, combine the flour, oat bran, brown sugar, and salt. Process briefly. Add the butter. Process until fine crumbs form. Slowly add the remaining water, 1 tablespoon at a time, until the mixture forms a ball.

Turn the mixture onto a floured surface. Divide in half. Roll each half into a rectangle 3" wide x 24" long. Spoon half of the fig mixture down the center of each rectangle. Carefully fold the sides over the fig mixture, pinching the edges together in the center. Cut into 1½"-long pieces. Place, pinched edges down, on the prepared baking sheets, leaving about 1½" between pieces.

Bake 1 sheet at a time for 10 minutes, or until lightly browned. Cool on a rack for 2 minutes. Remove from the sheet and place on the rack to cool completely.

Makes 32

Per bar: 100 calories, 2 g protein, 18 g carbohydrates, 3 g fat, 2 g saturated fat, 8 mg cholesterol, 50 mg sodium, 0 g dietary fiber

Exchanges: ½ starch, 1 fruit, ½ other carbohydrate, ½ fat

Coconut-Cherry Bars

½ cup trans-free margarine

1 package (12 ounces) white chocolate chips

2 eggs

⅓ cup sugar

1 cup unbleached flour

½ teaspoon salt

½ teaspoon almond extract

½ cup sweetened shredded coconut

½ cup cherry preserves

¼ cup sliced almonds

Coat a 5-quart or larger slow cooker with cooking spray.

In a saucepan over low heat, melt the margarine. Remove the pan from the heat and add 1 cup of the chocolate chips. Do not stir. Set aside.

In a medium bowl using an electric mixer on medium speed, beat the eggs until foamy. Gradually mix in the sugar, reserved margarine mixture, flour, salt, and almond extract. Mix just until blended. Spread one-quarter of the batter into the cooker. Cover. Cook on high for 15 to 20 minutes. Add the coconut and the remaining chocolate chips to the rest of the batter.

In another saucepan, melt the preserves over low heat. When the crust is finished cooking, evenly spread the preserves, then the remaining batter over the top.

Cover. Cook on low for 3 to 4 hours, or until the batter is just set. Turn off the cooker, sprinkle with the almonds, and let stand, uncovered, for 1 to 2 hours, or until completely cool, before cutting into bars.

Makes 16

Per bar: 248 calories, 3 g protein, 30 g carbohydrates, 13 g fat, 6 g saturated fat, 35 mg cholesterol, 152 mg sodium, 1 g dietary fiber

Exchanges: ½ starch, ½ other carbohydrate, 1½ fat

Pumpkin Spice Bars

1½   cups unbleached flour

1   cup whole wheat flour

1½   teaspoons baking soda

½   cup sugar

1   tablespoon ground cinnamon

½   teaspoon ground cloves

½   teaspoon ground nutmeg

⅔   cup molasses

2   egg whites

1   cup water

½   cup canned pumpkin

½   cup raisins

¼   cup walnuts

Preheat the oven to 350°F. Coat a 13" x 9" baking pan with cooking spray.

In a large bowl, combine the unbleached flour, whole wheat flour, baking soda, sugar, cinnamon, cloves, and nutmeg. Add the molasses, egg whites, water, and pumpkin and stir until thoroughly mixed. Stir in the raisins and walnuts. Spread evenly in the prepared pan.

Bake for 25 to 30 minutes, or until a wooden pick inserted in the center comes out clean. Cool in the pan and cut into 2" squares.

Makes 24

Per bar: 109 calories, 2 g protein, 24 g carbohydrates, 1 g fat, 1 g saturated fat, 0 mg cholesterol, 100 mg sodium, 1 g dietary fiber

Exchanges: ½ starch, ½ other carbohydrate

Variation

A dollop of fat-free whipped topping makes a tasty and pretty addition.

Lemon Bars

Photograph
on page 153

2¼ cups whole grain pastry flour

⅔ cup + 2 tablespoons confectioners' sugar

8 tablespoons chilled butter, cut into small pieces

3 lemons

1½ cups granulated sugar

1 cup liquid egg substitute

Preheat the oven to 350°F. Coat a 15" x 11" jelly-roll pan with cooking spray.

In a medium bowl, combine 2 cups of the flour, ⅔ cup of the confectioners' sugar, and the butter. Mix with your fingers to form crumbs. Press firmly and evenly into the bottom of the prepared pan.

Bake for 10 to 15 minutes, or until lightly browned. Cool on a rack.

Grate the rind from 2 of the lemons into a medium bowl. Cut all 3 lemons in half and squeeze the juice into the bowl. Whisk in the granulated sugar, the remaining ¼ cup flour, and egg substitute until smooth. Pour over the prepared crust.

Bake for 18 to 20 minutes, or until the filling is set when lightly touched in the center. Cool on a rack. Dust with the remaining 2 tablespoons confectioners' sugar before serving.

Makes 36

Per bar: 100 calories, 2 g protein, 17 g carbohydrates, 3 g fat, 2 g saturated fat, 5 mg cholesterol, 40 mg sodium, 0 g dietary fiber

Exchanges: 1 other carbohydrate, ½ fat

Apricot Squares

Photograph
on page 151

¾ *cup butter, at room temperature*

1½ *cups packed light brown sugar*

2½ *cups whole grain pastry flour*

1 *jar (12 ounces) apricot all-fruit preserves*

2 *eggs*

1 *teaspoon vanilla extract*

½ *teaspoon baking powder*

½ *teaspoon salt*

1 *tablespoon confectioners' sugar*

Preheat the oven to 325°F. Coat a 13" x 9" baking dish with cooking spray.

Place the butter and ½ cup of the brown sugar in a large bowl. Using an electric mixer on medium speed, beat until light and creamy. On low speed, gradually beat in 2 cups of the flour to get coarse crumbs. Press firmly and evenly into the bottom of the prepared baking dish. Spread the preserves over the top.

In a medium bowl, combine the eggs and the remaining 1 cup brown sugar. Beat on high speed until thick. Beat in the vanilla extract, baking powder, and salt. On low speed, gradually beat in the remaining ½ cup flour. Spread over the preserves.

Bake for 40 minutes, or until lightly browned. Cool on a rack. Dust with the confectioners' sugar before serving.

Makes 24

Per square: 176 calories, 2 g protein, 30 g carbohydrates, 6 g fat, 4 g saturated fat, 35 mg cholesterol, 130 mg sodium, 1 g dietary fiber

Exchanges: ½ starch, 1½ other carbohydrate, 1 fat

Chocolate Almond Fudge Brownies

Photograph on page 155

¾   cup (6 ounces) fat-free plain yogurt

1   cup whole grain pastry flour

⅔   cup unsweetened cocoa powder

½   teaspoon salt

1   egg

2   egg whites

2   cups sugar

½   teaspoon almond extract

¼   cup miniature semisweet chocolate chips

Line a sieve with a coffee filter or white paper towel and place over a deep bowl. Place the yogurt in the sieve and set aside to drain for 30 minutes. (You should have about ½ cup drained yogurt.) Discard the liquid in the bowl.

Preheat the oven to 350°F. Coat an 11" x 7" baking dish with cooking spray.

In a medium bowl, mix the flour, cocoa powder, and salt.

Place the egg and egg whites in a large bowl. Using an electric mixer on medium speed, beat until frothy. Add the sugar, almond extract, and yogurt. Beat until the sugar dissolves. Add the flour mixture and beat on low speed just until combined. Stir in the chocolate chips.

Pour into the prepared baking dish.

Bake for 30 minutes, or until a wooden pick inserted in the center comes out clean. Cool on a rack.

Makes 15

Per brownie: 159 calories, 3 g protein, 36 g carbohydrates, 2 g fat, 1 g saturated fat, 15 mg cholesterol, 95 mg sodium, 2 g dietary fiber

Exchanges: ½ starch, 1½ other carbohydrate, ½ fat

Baking Tip: To make cutting sticky desserts easier, remove them from the pan and slice with unwaxed dental floss. Cut a piece of floss several inches longer than the dessert that you're cutting. Hold the floss taut over the dessert, then lower your hands so the floss cuts through it. Let go of one end and pull the floss out through the other side.

Raspberry Swirl Brownies

1⅔	cups confectioners' sugar
½	cup whole grain pastry flour
¼	cup unsweetened cocoa powder
¾	teaspoon baking powder
⅛	teaspoon salt
1½	ounces unsweetened chocolate
2½	tablespoons canola oil
2	egg whites
2	tablespoons raspberry all-fruit preserves
2	teaspoons raspberry liqueur or vanilla extract
1	cup raspberries

Preheat the oven to 350°F. Line a 9" x 9" baking dish with foil, wrapping the excess foil over the handles. Coat with cooking spray.

In a medium bowl, mix the confectioners' sugar, flour, cocoa powder, baking powder, and salt.

In a large microwaveable bowl, combine the chocolate and oil. Microwave on high power for 1 minute. Stir until the chocolate is completely melted. Stir in the egg whites, preserves, and raspberry liqueur or vanilla extract. Stir in the flour mixture just until blended. Fold in the raspberries.

Pour the batter into the prepared baking dish and spread evenly.

Bake for 22 to 26 minutes, or until the center of the surface is almost firm when tapped. Cool on a rack for 15 minutes. Using the overhanging foil as handles, lift the brownies from the pan and place on a rack to cool completely.

Makes 12

Per brownie: 144 calories, 2 g protein, 25 g carbohydrates, 5 g fat, 2 g saturated fat, 0 mg cholesterol, 65 mg sodium, 2 g dietary fiber

Exchanges: ½ starch, 1 other carbohydrate, 1 fat

Chocolate–Peanut Butter Balls

25   *chocolate wafer cookies, finely crushed*

1   *cup + 2 tablespoons confectioners' sugar*

⅓   *cup honey*

¼   *cup + 2 tablespoons creamy peanut butter*

In a large bowl, mix the cookie crumbs and 1 cup of the confectioners' sugar.

In a medium bowl, whisk together the honey and peanut butter until well combined. Add to the cookie crumb mixture and stir well. (The mixture may be crumbly at this point.)

With your hands, shape the mixture into 1" balls. (The mixture should hold together as you shape it.)

Set the balls aside at room temperature until ready to serve or store them in an airtight container at room temperature for 2 to 3 days. Just before serving, roll the balls in the remaining 2 tablespoons confectioners' sugar.

Makes 36

Per ball: 58 calories, 1 g protein, 10 g carbohydrates, 2 g fat, 1 g saturated fat, 0 mg cholesterol, 40 mg sodium, 0 g dietary fiber

Exchanges: ½ other carbohydrate, ½ fat

Smoothies and Shakes

Just when you thought ice cream couldn't get any better, along came the milk shake, followed shortly by its healthful alternative, the smoothie. Thick, sweet, and naturally low in fat, smoothies make a great treat anytime you need a quick, healthy snack. These fresh-fruit milk shakes blend your favorite fruits with juices and low-fat dairy to create delicious beverages that are chock-full of nutrients and great on the go. Even if you splurge on one of our yummy chocolate or peanut butter shakes, you'll see that the recipes have been made healthier by using 2% milk, fat-free or low-fat yogurt, and cocoa powder.

Berry Berry Smoothie

¾   cup unsweetened pineapple juice

½   cup frozen unsweetened raspberries

½   cup frozen unsweetened strawberries

1   cup (8 ounces) fat-free vanilla yogurt

In a blender, combine the juice, raspberries, strawberries, and yogurt. Blend until smooth.

Makes 2 servings

Per serving: 195 calories, 8 g protein, 45 g carbohydrates, 1 g fat, 0 g saturated fat, 0 mg cholesterol, 85 mg sodium, 2 g dietary fiber

Exchanges: 1½ fruit, 1½ other carbohydrate

Mango Smoothie

1   can (8 ounces) juice-packed pineapple chunks

1   cup (8 ounces) fat-free frozen vanilla yogurt

1   large mango, peeled and chopped

1   ripe banana, sliced

Crushed or cracked ice

Cooking Tip:

Because mangoes are so juicy, they're messy to peel. They also have a pit in the center that makes cutting them tricky. Use a sharp knife to cut the flesh away from both sides of the large flat pit. Then cut the flesh from the skin.

In a blender, combine the pineapple (with juice), frozen yogurt, mango, and banana. Blend until smooth.

With the blender running, gradually drop in enough ice to bring the level up to 4 cups. Blend until the ice is pureed.

Makes 2 servings

Per serving: 256 calories, 8 g protein, 60 g carbohydrates, 1 g fat, 0 g saturated fat, 0 mg cholesterol, 85 mg sodium, 4 g dietary fiber

Exchanges: 2½ fruit, 1½ other carbohydrate

Peach-Pear Smoothie

1   cup cold peach nectar

2   pears, peeled, cored, and chopped

1   cup 2% milk or unsweetened soy milk

⅛   teaspoon ground nutmeg

In a blender, combine the nectar, pears, and soy milk. Blend until smooth. Serve sprinkled with the nutmeg.

Makes 4 servings

Per serving: 103 calories, 2 g protein, 22 g carbohydrates, 2 g fat, 1 g saturated fat, 0 mg cholesterol, 11 mg sodium, 3 g dietary fiber

Exchanges: 1½ fruit, 1½ lean meat

Peachy Smoothie

1   cup fat-free vanilla ice cream

½   cup orange juice

1   large peach, pitted, peeled, and sliced

1   tablespoon sugar

    Pinch of ground cinnamon

In a blender, combine the ice cream, orange juice, peach, sugar, and cinnamon. Blend until smooth.

Makes 2 servings

Per serving: 162 calories, 4 g protein, 37 g carbohydrates, 0 g fat, 0 g saturated fat, 0 mg cholesterol, 65 mg sodium, 2 g dietary fiber

Exchanges: 1 fruit, 1½ other carbohydrate

Strawberry-Kiwi Smoothie

1¼ *cups cold apple juice*

1 *ripe banana, sliced*

1 *kiwifruit, peeled and sliced*

5 *frozen strawberries*

1½ *teaspoons honey*

In a blender, combine the juice, banana, kiwifruit, strawberries, and honey. Blend until smooth.

Makes 4 servings

Per serving: 72 calories, 1 g protein, 18 g carbohydrates, 0 g fat, 0 g saturated fat, 0 mg cholesterol, 0 mg sodium, 2 g dietary fiber

Exchanges: 1 fruit

Banana-Blueberry Smoothie

¾ *cup part-skim ricotta cheese*

¼ *cup 1% percent milk*

½ *cup blueberries*

½ *banana*

6 *ice cubes*

In a blender, combine the ricotta cheese, milk, blueberries, banana, and ice cubes. Puree until smooth.

Makes 2 servings

Per serving: 180 calories, 12 g protein, 18 g carbohydrates, 8 g fat, 5 g saturated fat, 30 mg cholesterol, 132 mg sodium, 2 g dietary fiber

Exchanges: 1 fruit, 1 fat, 1½ meat

Pomegranate Smoothie

1 cup pomegranate juice
1 banana
½ cup low-fat kefir

In a blender, combine the juice, banana, and kefir. Pulse on high power until smooth.

Makes 2 servings

Per serving: 162 calories, 3 g protein, 35 g carbohydrates, 2 g fat, 0 g saturated fat, 0 mg cholesterol, 42 mg sodium, 2 g dietary fiber
Exchanges: 2 fruit, ½ fat

Pumpkin Smoothie

1 cup canned pumpkin
1 cup vanilla soy milk
1 cup crushed ice
2 tablespoons honey
2 teaspoons pumpkin pie spice

HEALTH BONUS:
This smoothie tastes like pie in a glass, and each 8-ounce cup provides 100 percent of the Daily Value for beta-carotene, which is an antioxidant that fights cancer.

In a blender, combine the pumpkin, soy milk, ice, honey, and pumpkin pie spice. Pulse on high power until smooth.

Makes 2 servings

Per serving: 162 calories, 5 g protein, 34 g carbohydrates, 2 g fat, 0 g saturated fat, 0 mg cholesterol, 55 mg sodium, 4 g dietary fiber
Exchanges: ½ starch, ½ milk, 1 other carbohydrate, ½ fat

Caribbean Fruit Frappé

1½   cups chopped pineapple
1   cup low-fat vanilla ice cream
1   mango, peeled and chopped
2   tablespoons lime juice
½   teaspoon coconut extract

Cooking Tip:

Coconut extract is available in the spice section of most supermarkets. You can replace it with ½ teaspoon rum extract or vanilla extract.

In a blender, combine the pineapple, ice cream, mango, lime juice, and coconut extract. Blend until smooth.

Makes 4 servings

Per serving: 78 calories, 2 g protein, 15 g carbohydrates, 2 g fat, 1 g saturated fat, 5 mg cholesterol, 30 mg sodium, 1 g dietary fiber

Exchanges: ½ fruit, ½ other carbohydrate

Blueberry–Peanut Butter Shake

2   cups fat-free milk
2   tablespoons ground flaxseed
2   tablespoons natural creamy no-salt-added peanut butter
1   cup frozen blueberries

In a blender, combine the milk, flaxseed, peanut butter, and blueberries. Blend until smooth.

Makes 2 servings

Per serving: 252 calories, 14 g protein, 20 g carbohydrates, 10 g fat, 1 g saturated fat, 5 mg cholesterol, 164 mg sodium, 6 g dietary fiber

Exchanges: 1 milk, ½ fruit, 1½ fat, ½ very lean meat

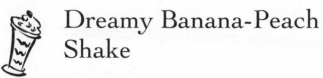

Dreamy Banana-Peach Shake

½   cup frozen banana slices
½   cup frozen peach slices
½   cup fat-free milk
1   teaspoon honey

> **Cooking Tip:**
> Keep bananas and strawberries in the freezer so you'll always be ready to whip up refreshing drinks.

In a blender, combine the bananas, peaches, milk, and honey. Blend until smooth.

Makes 1 serving

Per serving: 170 calories, 6 g protein, 39 g carbohydrates, 1 g fat, 0 g saturated fat, 0 mg cholesterol, 65 mg sodium, 4 g dietary fiber

Exchanges: 2 fruit, ½ milk

Creamy Frozen Shake

1   cup frozen banana slices, peach slices, or strawberries
½   cup orange juice
½   cup fat-free vanilla yogurt

In a blender, combine the bananas, peaches, or strawberries; the orange juice; and yogurt. Blend until smooth.

Makes 1 serving

Per serving: 236 calories, 9 g protein, 46 g carbohydrates, 3 g fat, 2 g saturated fat, 10 mg cholesterol, 125 mg sodium, 4 g dietary fiber

Exchanges: 2 fruit, 1 milk

Peanut Butter Ice Cream Shake

Photograph on page 76

1	*pint fat-free frozen vanilla yogurt*
¼	*cup creamy peanut butter*
¼	*cup fat-free milk*
2	*tablespoons chocolate syrup*

In a blender, combine the frozen yogurt, peanut butter, milk, and chocolate syrup. Blend until smooth.

Makes 4 servings

Per serving: 112 calories, 5 g protein, 14 g carbohydrates, 4 g fat, 1 g saturated fat, 1 mg cholesterol, 79 mg sodium, 1 g dietary fiber

Exchanges: 1 other carbohydrate, 1 fat

Peanut Butter Breakfast Shake

1	*cup fat-free milk*
1	*banana, sliced*
2	*tablespoons creamy peanut butter*

In a blender, combine the milk, banana, and peanut butter. Blend until smooth.

Makes 1 serving

Per serving: 345 calories, 16 g protein, 37 g carbohydrates, 18 g fat, 4 g saturated fat, 4 mg cholesterol, 281 mg sodium, 6 g dietary fiber

Exchanges: 1 fruit, 1 milk, 1 lean meat, 3 fat

Chocolate–Peanut Butter Shake

1 tablespoons creamy peanut butter
10 ice cubes
2 cups chocolate soy milk
1 teaspoon vanilla extract

In a blender, combine the peanut butter, ice cubes, soy milk, and vanilla extract. Blend on high for about 30 seconds, until the shake is smooth and creamy.

Makes 2 servings

Per serving: 220 calories, 11 g protein, 18 g carbohydrates, 12 g fat, 2 g saturated fat, 0 mg cholesterol, 106 mg sodium, 4 g dietary fiber

Exchanges: 1 milk, 1 other carbohydrate, 2½ fat, ½ meat, ½ very lean meat

Breezy Chocolate Chip Milk Shake

5 cups low-fat mint chocolate chip ice cream, softened
⅓ cup fat-free milk
¼ cup fat-free fudge sauce

In a blender, combine the ice cream, milk, and fudge sauce. Blend until smooth.

Makes 8 servings

Per serving: 197 calories, 5 g protein, 38 g carbohydrates, 3 g fat, 2 g saturated fat, 7 mg cholesterol, 80 mg sodium, 0 g dietary fiber

Exchanges: 2 other carbohydrate, ½ fat

Banana Split Shake

Photograph on page 76

2	cups fat-free vanilla ice cream
½	cup fat-free milk
1	ripe banana, sliced
3	tablespoons fat-free fudge sauce
2	tablespoons chopped roasted peanuts or toasted walnuts

In a blender, combine the ice cream, milk, banana, and fudge sauce. Blend until smooth. Serve sprinkled with the peanuts or walnuts.

Makes 4 servings

Per serving: 361 calories, 12 g protein, 36 g carbohydrates, 3 g fat, 0 g saturated fat, 0 mg cholesterol, 90 mg sodium, 1 g dietary fiber

Exchanges: ½ fruit, 1½ other carbohydrate, ½ fat

Creamy Fruit Shake

1	cup 1% milk
⅓	frozen banana
½	cup chilled canned mango slices, drained
½	cup frozen strawberries
1	teaspoon sugar

In a blender, combine the milk, banana, mango, strawberries, and sugar. Blend until smooth.

Makes 1 serving

Per serving: 221 calories, 8 g protein, 47 g carbohydrates, 1 g fat, 0 g saturated fat, 2 mg cholesterol, 91 mg sodium, 0 g dietary fiber

Exchanges: 1 fruit, 2 other carbohydrate, ½ fat

Strawberry-Banana Soda

1½   cups sparkling mineral water
½   ripe banana, sliced and frozen
4   large strawberries, halved and frozen

In a blender, combine the water, banana, and strawberries. Blend until smooth.

Makes 2 servings

Per serving: 40 calories, 1 g protein, 10 g carbohydrates, 0 g fat, 0 g saturated fat, 0 mg cholesterol, 5 mg sodium, 2 g dietary fiber

Exchanges: ½ fruit

Iced Spiced Cocoa Latte

HEALTH BONUS:
Coffee may help ward off diabetes in women.

3   cups water
¼   teaspoon ground cinnamon
5   tablespoons freshly ground coffee
6   teaspoons sugar
3   teaspoons unsweetened cocoa powder
3   cups 1% milk
6   cinnamon sticks

Place the water in a coffeemaker. In a bowl, mix the cinnamon and coffee; brew one pot.

Pour equal amounts of coffee into 6 glasses filled with ice. Add 1 teaspoon sugar and ½ teaspoon cocoa powder to each. Mix well; top off with milk. Place in the refrigerator until chilled. Garnish with the cinnamon sticks.

Makes 6 servings

Per serving: 72 calories, 5 g protein, 11 g carbohydrates, 1 g fat, 1 g saturated fat, 6 mg cholesterol, 58 mg sodium, 0 g fiber

Exchanges: ½ milk

Fruit *and* Yogurt

Old conventional wisdom held that people with diabetes shouldn't eat fruit. Too much sugar, experts screamed! In fact, some people believed that eating sugar caused diabetes. Now we know that neither are the case. The American Diabetes Association encourages people with diabetes to have two to four servings of fruit a day, such as one small piece of fresh fruit or 2 tablespoons of dried fruit. Besides satisfying a sugar Jones, fruits provide important vitamins and minerals and fiber. The recipes in this section are bursting with fresh fruits. Many of them also offer yogurt, which is a great source of calcium to boot.

Chocolate Sauce

⅔   cup strong espresso coffee, cooled

¼   cup sugar

3   tablespoons unsweetened cocoa powder

2   teaspoons cornstarch

1   teaspoon vanilla extract

½   teaspoon butter

In a medium saucepan, combine the coffee, sugar, cocoa powder, and cornstarch. Whisk until smooth. Cook over medium heat, stirring constantly, until smooth and thickened. Stir in the vanilla extract and butter. Cool slightly before using.

Makes 12 servings

Per serving: 25 calories, 0 g protein, 6 g carbohydrates, 0 g fat, 0 g saturated fat, 0 mg cholesterol, 3 mg sodium, 1 g dietary fiber

Exchanges: ½ other carbohydrate

Variation

Replace the brewed espresso with 2/3 cup hot water mixed with 2 teaspoons instant espresso coffee powder.

Cooking Tip: This is delicious over fruit, such as berries, or desserts such as pound cake.

Chocolate-Tangerine Fondue

1   *can (14 ounces) fat-free sweetened condensed milk*

6   *ounces semisweet chocolate baking chips*

8   *tangerines, peeled and segmented*

In a heavy saucepan over very low heat, cook the milk and chocolate chips, stirring constantly until the chips melt (about 3 minutes). Transfer to a fondue pot and keep warm. Dip the tangerines into the sauce.

Makes 8 servings

Per serving: 286 calories, 5 g protein, 55 g carbohydrates, 7 g fat, 4 g saturated fat, 6 mg cholesterol, 55 mg sodium, 3 g dietary fiber

Exchanges: ½ fruit, 3 other carbohydrate, 1 fat

HEALTH BONUS:
University of California researchers report that ascorbic acid (found in citrus fruits) releases more of cocoa's heart-protective antioxidants. Study author Carl Keen, PhD, says that means you'll likely get more heart benefits from the naturally delicious pairing of chocolate with citrus fruit. So *Prevention* developed this fondue with tangerine recipe.

Frozen Chocolate-Banana Pops

4   *wooden sticks for making pops*

2   *bananas, halved crosswise*

½   *cup chocolate sauce (the kind that forms a shell)*

4   *tablespoons finely chopped unsalted peanuts*

Insert a wooden stick into the cut end of each banana piece. Pour the chocolate sauce over the bananas until they're completely coated, then roll the chocolate-coated bananas in the peanuts. Place pops in the freezer for at least 2 hours, or until frozen.

Makes 4 servings

Per serving: 316 calories, 4 g protein, 31 g carbohydrates, 22 g fat, 9 g saturated fat, 0 mg cholesterol, 21 mg sodium, 3 g dietary fiber

Exchanges: 1 fruit, 1 other carbohydrate, 4 fat

Bananas Foster

1   *tablespoon butter*

2   *tablespoons packed dark brown sugar*

2   *tablespoons apple juice concentrate*

¼   *teaspoon ground cinnamon*

3   *bananas*

2   *teaspoons vanilla extract*

3   *cups fat-free frozen vanilla yogurt*

Melt the butter in a large nonstick skillet over medium heat. Add the brown sugar, apple juice concentrate, and cinnamon. Cook, stirring, until the sugar melts.

Cut the bananas in half lengthwise, then crosswise. Add to the skillet and toss to coat well. Cook for 3 to 5 minutes, or until the bananas are tender. Remove from the heat. Add the vanilla extract. Swirl to combine.

Serve immediately over the frozen yogurt.

Makes 6 servings

Per serving: 198 calories, 5 g protein, 40 g carbohydrates, 2 g fat, 1 g saturated fat, 7 mg cholesterol, 87 mg sodium, 2 g dietary fiber

Exchanges: 1 fruit, 1½ other carbohydrate, ½ fat

Baked Bananas with Rum Sauce

5   tablespoons orange juice

3   tablespoons dark rum or 1½ teaspoons rum extract

3   tablespoons plum or blueberry fruit spread

2   tablespoons butter

4½   teaspoons lemon juice

⅛   teaspoon ground nutmeg

4   bananas, halved lengthwise

3   tablespoons coarsely chopped pecans

Preheat the oven to 400°F.

In a small saucepan, combine the orange juice, rum, fruit spread, butter, lemon juice, and nutmeg. Bring just to a boil over medium heat, stirring. Immediately remove from the heat.

Arrange the bananas, flat side down, in a single layer in a shallow baking dish. Pour the butter mixture over the bananas and sprinkle with the pecans. Bake until the bananas are tender and the sauce has thickened slightly, 12 to 15 minutes.

Makes 4 servings

Per serving: 305 calories, 3 g protein, 50 g carbohydrates, 10 g fat, 4 g saturated fat, 15 mg cholesterol, 42 mg sodium, 5 g dietary fiber

Exchanges: 2½ fruit, ½ other carbohydrate, 2 fat

Variation

Substitute apricot, cherry, or raspberry fruit spread for the plum or blueberry spread. Sprinkle with 1 tablespoon toasted unsweetened coconut.

Per serving: 312 calories, 3 g protein, 50 g carbohydrates, 11 g fat, 5 g saturated fat, 15 mg cholesterol, 43 mg sodium, 5 g dietary fiber

Exchanges: 2½ fruit, ½ other carbohydrate, 2 fat

Guiltless Banana Split

1   banana, sliced lengthwise

1   pineapple slice, cut into wedges

4   large strawberries

2   tablespoons chocolate syrup

1   tablespoon low-fat whipped topping

Place the banana halves on a plate. Top 1 half with the pineapple. Top the other half with the strawberries. Drizzle with the chocolate syrup and top with the whipped topping.

Makes 1 serving

Per serving: 301 calories, 3 g protein, 72 g carbohydrates, 3 g fat, 2 g saturated fat, 0 mg cholesterol, 45 mg sodium, 8 g dietary fiber

Exchanges: 3 fruit, 2 other carbohydrate, ½ fat

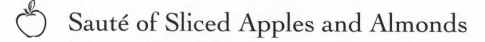

Sauté of Sliced Apples and Almonds

4	Granny Smith apples, peeled and cored
2	tablespoons lemon juice
1	teaspoon canola oil
¼	cup apple cider
1	tablespoon maple syrup
¼	teaspoon lemon rind
¼	teaspoon vanilla extract
¼	teaspoon ground cinnamon
¼	teaspoon ground cloves
2	tablespoons sliced almonds, toasted

Slice the apples and toss them with the lemon juice in a large bowl.

In a large nonstick skillet over medium-high heat, warm the oil. Add the apples and sauté for 2 minutes. Reduce the heat to low, cover, and simmer, stirring occasionally, for 5 to 8 minutes, or until the apples are just tender. Using a slotted spoon, carefully remove the apples and divide among 4 dessert dishes.

To the skillet, add the apple cider, maple syrup, lemon rind, vanilla extract, cinnamon, and cloves. Cook over medium-high heat, stirring constantly, until syrupy. Spoon over the apples. Sprinkle with the almonds.

Makes 4 servings

Per serving: 113 calories, 1 g protein, 23 g carbohydrates, 3 g fat, 0 g saturated fat, 0 mg cholesterol, 3 mg sodium, 2 g dietary fiber

Exchanges: 1 fruit, ½ fat

Variation

Sauté of Sliced Pears and Almonds: Replace the apples with 5 pears, the apple cider with ¼ cup orange juice, and the lemon rind with 1 teaspoon orange rind.

Per serving: 171 calories, 2 g protein, 39 g carbohydrates, 3 g fat, 0 g saturated fat, 0 mg cholesterol, 3 mg sodium, 7 g dietary fiber

Exchanges: 2 fruit, ½ fat

Baked Apple Halves with Maple Cream

2   large Ida Red apples, halved lengthwise and cored with a melon
    baller

4   teaspoons trans-free margarine, cut into small pieces

½   cup orange juice

1   tablespoon apple cider vinegar

¼   cup evaporated milk

2   tablespoons maple syrup

Preheat the oven to 350°F. Chill a small mixing bowl.

Place the apples flesh side up in an 8" x 8" (or 8" round) baking dish and dot with the margarine. Pour the orange juice and vinegar over the top, cover with foil, and bake for 40 to 45 minutes, until the apples are soft but still hold their shape.

Remove the apples to a large plate and pour the juice from the dish into a small saucepan. Bring to a boil and reduce for 3 to 4 minutes until thick and syrupy. Reserve 4 tablespoons.

Using an electric mixer on high speed, in the chilled bowl, whip the milk and maple syrup together for 3 to 5 minutes, until the mixture thickens.

Top each baked apple half with 1½ tablespoons of the maple cream and drizzle with 1 tablespoon of the reserved fruit syrup.

Makes 4 servings

Per serving: 145 calories, 2 g protein, 27 g carbohydrates, 5 g fat, 2 g saturated fat, 5 mg cholesterol, 51 mg sodium, 3 g dietary fiber

Exchanges: 1 fruit, ½ other carbohydrate, 1 fat

Baking Tips: Bake the apples for this delicious dessert up to a day ahead, cool, and store them in the refrigerator, covered. If Ida Reds are unavailable, use Jonathan or Jonagold.

Cinnamon-Ginger Applesauce

4   large Empire apples, peeled and cut into 1" cubes

½   cup water

2   tablespoons light brown sugar

2   tablespoons freshly squeezed lemon juice

¼   teaspoon ground ginger

¼   teaspoon freshly grated lemon rind

⅛   teaspoon ground cinnamon

Place the apples, water, brown sugar, lemon juice, ginger, lemon rind, and cinnamon in a 2-quart saucepan and bring to a boil. Lower the heat to a simmer, partially cover, and cook for 20 minutes. Mash with a potato masher or fork and cook, uncovered, for 5 to 10 minutes longer until thick.

Makes 4 servings

Per serving: 121 calories, 1 g protein, 32 g carbohydrates, 0 g fat, 0 g saturated fat, 0 mg cholesterol, 4 mg sodium, 3 g dietary fiber

Exchanges: 1½ fruit, ½ other carbohydrate

Cooking Tip: Because the flesh of Empire apples breaks down easily, they're perfect for making this classic sauce. Their flavor is similar to McIntosh or Crispin.

Savory Grilled Peaches

8   peaches, halved and pitted

1   tablespoon toasted walnut oil

Freshly ground black pepper (optional)

¼   cup poppy seed salad dressing (optional)

Preheat the grill to medium.

Brush the peaches on all sides with the oil. Place on the grill cut side down and grill for 10 to 12 minutes, turning once, or until heated through but still holding their shape. Remove the peels, if desired. Sprinkle with the pepper (if using) or serve with the dressing (if using).

Makes 8 servings

Per serving: 53 calories, 1 g protein, 9 g carbohydrates, 2 g fat, 0 g saturated fat, 0 mg cholesterol, 0 mg sodium, 2 g dietary fiber

Exchanges: ½ fruit, ½ fat

Broiled Peaches and Strawberries

5   medium peaches, cut into 1" wedges

1½   pints strawberries, hulled and quartered

2   tablespoons honey

½   teaspoon ground cinnamon

⅛   teaspoon ground allspice or cloves

1   tablespoon butter, cut into small pieces

3   tablespoons slivered fresh mint, lemon verbena, or cinnamon basil (optional)

Preheat the broiler. Coat a large baking sheet with sides with cooking spray.

In a large bowl, combine the peaches, strawberries, honey, cinnamon, and allspice or cloves and toss to coat well. Place the fruit on the prepared baking sheet. Dot with the butter.

Broil, turning the pan 2 or 3 times (no need to turn the fruit), for 4 minutes, or until the fruit is glazed, bubbly, and golden brown in spots. Remove from the oven and let cool slightly.

Sprinkle with the mint, lemon verbena, or cinnamon basil (if using). Serve warm or at room temperature.

Makes 6 servings

Per serving: 94 calories, 1 g protein, 19 g carbohydrates, 2 g fat, 1 g saturated fat, 5 mg cholesterol, 15 mg sodium, 3 g dietary fiber

Exchanges: 1 fruit, ½ other carbohydrate, ½ fat

Roasted Pears with Goat Cheese

2   tablespoons butter

¼   cup sugar

1   tablespoon lemon juice

4   large ripe pears, halved and cored

¼   cup seedless raspberry all-fruit preserves

¼   teaspoon coarsely ground black pepper

2   ounces goat cheese

Preheat the oven to 450°F. Coat a 13" x 9" baking dish with cooking spray.

While the oven is preheating, place the butter in the prepared dish. Place in the oven for about 5 minutes, or until the butter is melted. Remove from the oven and stir in the sugar and lemon juice.

Place the pears in the dish and turn to coat with the butter mixture. Arrange cut side up, making sure there is some butter in the cavities.

Bake for 20 to 25 minutes, or until the pears are very tender. Transfer the pears to 4 dessert dishes.

In a small saucepan, combine the preserves and pepper. Pour the juices from the baking dish into the pan and stir to combine. Bring to a boil over medium heat, stirring occasionally. Continue to boil for 2 to 3 minutes, or until the sauce is slightly thickened.

To serve, spoon some goat cheese into the cavity in each pear, then drizzle the raspberry sauce over the pears.

Makes 4 servings

Per serving: 293 calories, 4 g protein, 52 g carbohydrates, 10 g fat, 6 g saturated fat, 22 mg cholesterol, 117 mg sodium, 4 g dietary fiber

Exchanges: 2 fruit, 1½ other carbohydrate, ½ lean meat, 1½ fat

Summer Fruit Compote

1   cup water

1   package (6 ounces) mixed whole dried fruit

3   tablespoons frozen orange juice concentrate

2   tablespoons packed light brown sugar

3   whole allspice berries

1   bay leaf

1   stick cinnamon or a pinch of ground cinnamon

3   medium peaches, cut into ¾" wedges

3   medium plums, cut into ¾" wedges

1   cup pitted sweet white or red cherries (optional)

In a large saucepan, combine the water, dried fruit, orange juice concentrate, brown sugar, allspice berries, bay leaf, and cinnamon stick or ground cinnamon. Bring to a boil over high heat. Reduce the heat to low, cover, and simmer, stirring occasionally, for 10 minutes, or until the fruit is very tender.

Add the peaches and plums. Cover and simmer for 5 minutes, or until the peaches and plums are tender but not mushy. Stir in the cherries (if using) and cook for 3 minutes. Remove from the heat and place in a serving bowl. Let stand for at least 1 hour, or until the fruit has cooled and the flavors have blended. Remove and discard the bay leaf and cinnamon stick before serving.

Makes 6 servings

Per serving: 147 calories, 2 g protein, 38 g carbohydrates, 0 g fat, 0 g saturated fat, 0 mg cholesterol, 8 mg sodium, 4 g dietary fiber

Exchanges: 2 fruit

Quick Apple-Orange Compote

1   *Granny Smith apple, cored and chopped*

1   *navel orange, peeled and chopped*

1   *teaspoon ground cinnamon*

½   *cup (8 ounces) fat-free vanilla yogurt*

2   *tablespoons pecan or walnut pieces*

In a medium microwaveable bowl, combine the apple, orange, and cinnamon. Cover with plastic wrap and microwave on high for 4 minutes, or until the fruit is hot and soft. Divide between 2 bowls and spoon the yogurt evenly over each. Sprinkle with the nuts and serve warm.

Makes 2 servings

Per serving: 175 calories, 5 g protein, 30 g carbohydrates, 6 g fat, 1 g saturated fat, 1 mg cholesterol, 44 mg sodium, 4 g dietary fiber

Exchanges: 1 fruit, ½ other carbohydrate, 1 fat

Marinated Summer Berries

1   pint raspberries

1   pint blueberries

1   pint blackberries, olallieberries, or boysenberries

3   cups sparkling cider or dry champagne

1   cup club soda

Place the raspberries, blueberries, and blackberries, olallieberries, or boysenberries in a medium bowl. Pour the cider or champagne and club soda over the berries and let stand for about 1 hour.

Makes 6 servings

Per serving: 130 calories, 2 g protein, 32 g carbohydrates, 1 g fat, 0 g saturated fat, 0 mg cholesterol, 22 mg sodium, 6 g dietary fiber

Exchanges: 2 fruit,

Variation

This recipe works well with almost any combination of berries. Try replacing the raspberries with strawberries and/or loganberries. For a hint of spice, sprinkle the marinated berries with a pinch of ground cinnamon.

HEALTH BONUS:

Olallieberries look like blackberries, but they're actually a cross between a loganberry and youngberry. Like all berries, they're high in fiber, which has been shown to protect against cancer.

Broiled Pineapple with Ginger-Yogurt Sauce

½   cup (4 ounces) plain yogurt

1½   teaspoons chopped crystallized ginger

1   teaspoon vanilla extract

1   teaspoon grated orange rind

2   tablespoons butter

4½   teaspoons lime juice

2   tablespoons unsweetened peach or apricot fruit spread

½   cored, peeled pineapple, cut into wedges 1½" thick

Place a broiler rack 4" from the heat source and preheat the broiler.

In a small bowl, combine the yogurt, ginger, vanilla extract, and orange rind. Cover and set aside.

In a small skillet, combine the butter, lime juice, and fruit spread. Cook over low heat until the butter and fruit spread are melted.

Place the pineapple in a broiler-safe 11" x 7" baking pan. Pour the butter mixture over the wedges and toss to coat. Arrange in a single layer.

Broil, turning once, until lightly browned on both sides, 5 to 7 minutes, shaking the pan occasionally so the juices don't burn. Remove the wedges and juices to 4 bowls, and serve hot or warm topped with the yogurt sauce.

Makes 4 servings

Per serving: 131 calories, 2 g protein, 17 g carbohydrates, 7 g fat, 4 g saturated fat, 19 mg cholesterol, 56 mg sodium, 1 g dietary fiber

Exchanges: ½ fruit, ½ other carbohydrate, 1½ fat

Variation

To grill the pineapple, toss the pineapple wedges with the butter mixture and thread onto skewers. Grill over a medium-low fire until tender, basting with the remaining butter mixture.

Dried Apricot Fool

1	cup (6 ounces) dried apricots
¾	cup orange juice
1	teaspoon lemon juice
1	teaspoon grated orange rind
1	tablespoon + 1½ teaspoons rum or ½ teaspoon rum extract (optional)
⅓	cup heavy cream
3	tablespoons slivered or sliced almonds, toasted
⅛	teaspoon ground nutmeg

Combine the apricots and orange juice in a saucepan over low heat. Bring to a simmer, partially cover, and cook until the fruit is very tender, about 15 minutes. Pour the fruit and liquid into a food processor and process until smooth, 2 to 3 minutes. Remove to a large bowl, stir in the lemon juice, orange rind, and rum or extract (if using) and let cool.

In a large bowl, whip the cream to soft but firm peaks. Stir one-quarter of the cream into the apricot mixture. Gently fold in the rest until evenly incorporated. Remove to a serving bowl and chill for at least 3 hours or up to 3 days. Serve sprinkled with the almonds and nutmeg.

Makes 4 servings

Per serving: 236 calories, 3 g protein, 34 g carbohydrates, 11 g fat, 5 g saturated fat, 27 mg cholesterol, 15 mg sodium, 4 g dietary fiber

Exchanges: 2 fruit, 2 fat

Variation

Replace the apricots with dried mangoes or other dried fruit.

Per serving: 282 calories, 2 g protein, 44 g carbohydrates, 11 g fat, 5 g saturated fat, 27 mg cholesterol, 33 mg sodium, 2 g dietary fiber

Exchanges: 3 fruit, 2 fat

🍎 Berry Parfaits

2   *cups blackberries, raspberries, blueberries,*
    or strawberries

2   *tablespoons honey*

1   *cup (8 ounces) fat-free lemon yogurt*

Set 4 berries aside for garnish. Place the remainder in a blender. Add the honey and process until smooth.

Evenly layer the berry mixture and the yogurt in 4 parfait glasses. Garnish with the reserved berries.

Makes 4 servings

Per serving: 121 calories, 4 g protein, 28 g carbohydrates, 0 g fat, 0 g saturated fat, 0 mg cholesterol, 40 mg sodium, 4 g dietary fiber

Exchanges: ½ fruit, 1½ other carbohydrate

Granola-Berry Parfaits

3   *cups old-fashioned rolled oats*

½   *cup slivered almonds*

¼   *cup wheat germ*

2   *tablespoons sunflower seeds*

1   *teaspoon ground cinnamon*

5   *tablespoons honey*

4   *cups (32 ounces) low-fat maple vanilla yogurt or vanilla yogurt*

2   *cups raspberries, blueberries, or sliced strawberries*

Preheat the oven to 325°F. Coat a 15" x 11" jelly-roll pan with cooking spray.

In a medium bowl, mix the oats, almonds, wheat germ, sunflower seeds, and cinnamon. Drizzle with the honey and stir to coat well. Spread in an even layer in the prepared pan.

Bake, stirring occasionally, for 30 minutes, or until golden brown. Cool on a rack.

To serve, layer the granola, yogurt, and berries in 8 parfait glasses.

Makes 8 servings

Per serving: 363 calories, 13 g protein, 61 g carbohydrates, 8 g fat, 1 g saturated fat, 7 mg cholesterol, 79 mg sodium, 7 g dietary fiber

Exchanges: 1½ starch, 2 other carbohydrate, ½ lean meat, 1½ fat

Baking Tip: Granola can be prepared ahead of time and stored in an airtight container for several days.

Mixed Berries with Creamy Yogurt

2   cups (16 ounces) fat-free plain yogurt
2   cups fresh or frozen unsweetened mixed berries
2   packets Splenda (optional)
1   teaspoon vanilla extract (optional)

Line a 2-cup mesh strainer with a paper coffee filter and place it over a mixing bowl. Fill the filter with the yogurt, cover with a clean cloth or waxed paper, and set the bowl (with strainer inside) in the refrigerator for several hours. Much of the liquid from the yogurt will drain into the bowl, resulting in thicker yogurt. In a blender, puree the berries along with the Splenda and vanilla extract (if using). Once the yogurt has drained, place it in a large bowl and stir in the berry puree.

Makes 4 servings

Per serving: 80 calories, 6 g protein, 18 g carbohydrates, 0 g fat, 0 g saturated fat, 3 mg cholesterol, 69 mg sodium, 2 g dietary fiber

Exchanges: ½ milk, ½ fruit

Cooking Tip: This is like Greek yogurt because it is drained. If you find it to be bitter, add the optional Splenda and vanilla extract.

HEALTH BONUS:
Each serving of this dish contains ½ cup of yogurt, which boasts 225 milligrams of calcium. The moo mineral is key in fighting diabetes. Harvard University researchers found that for every daily serving of low-fat dairy foods people ate a day, their risk of developing type 2 diabetes dropped by 9 percent.

Banana Ice Cream

  2   large frozen bananas, sliced
  2   tablespoons sugar
1½   cups fat-free milk
  ½   teaspoon ground cinnamon
  ½   teaspoon vanilla extract
       Ground nutmeg

In a food processor or blender, combine the bananas, sugar, and ½ cup of the milk. Puree until smooth. Add the cinnamon, vanilla extract, and remaining 1 cup milk. Puree until smooth.

Transfer the mixture to a metal or plastic container. Cover and freeze for 4 hours or overnight. Remove from the freezer and break up the mixture with a knife. Process briefly in a food processor or blender.

Return to the container, cover, and freeze for at least 30 minutes before serving. Sprinkle with the nutmeg.

Makes 4 servings

Per serving: 119 calories, 4 g protein, 27 g carbohydrates, ½ g fat, 0 g saturated fat, 0 mg cholesterol, 49 mg sodium, 2 g dietary fiber

Exchanges: ½ milk, 1 fruit, ½ other carbohydrate

Variation

Berry-Banana Ice Cream: Add 1 cup frozen blueberries, strawberries, or raspberries along with the bananas.

Per serving: 139 calories, 4 g protein, 31 g carbohydrates, 1 g fat, 0 g saturated fat, 2 mg cholesterol, 49 mg sodium, 3 g dietary fiber

Exchanges: ½ starch, 1½ fruit, ½ other carbohydrate

Blueberry-Buttermilk Sorbet

1   *package (12 ounces) frozen blueberries*

½   *cup frozen white grape juice concentrate*

⅓   *cup sugar*

1   *teaspoon grated lemon rind*

1   *cup buttermilk*

In a small saucepan, combine the blueberries, frozen juice concentrate, sugar, and lemon rind. Bring to a boil over high heat. Reduce the heat to medium-low and simmer for 5 minutes, or until the blueberries are thawed and begin to pop. Remove the pan from the heat; set aside to cool.

In a food processor or blender, combine the buttermilk and the blueberry mixture. Puree until smooth.

Transfer the mixture to a metal or plastic container. Cover and freeze for 4 hours or overnight. Remove from the freezer and break up the mixture with a knife. Process briefly in a food processor or blender.

Return to the container, cover, and freeze for at least 30 minutes before serving.

Makes 4 servings

Per serving: 166 calories, 3 g protein, 38 g carbohydrates, 1 g fat, 0 g saturated fat, 3 mg cholesterol, 84 mg sodium, 2 g dietary fiber

Exchanges: ½ fruit, 1½ other carbohydrate

Melon Sorbet

4   cups frozen cantaloupe, honeydew, or watermelon chunks, slightly thawed

1   frozen banana, sliced

1   teaspoon lemon juice

In a food processor or blender, combine the melon, banana, and lemon juice. Process until smooth.

Transfer the mixture to a metal or plastic container. Cover and freeze for 4 hours or overnight. Remove from the freezer and break up the mixture with a knife. Process briefly in a food processor or blender.

Return to the container, cover, and freeze for at least 30 minutes before serving.

Makes 6 servings

Per serving: 54 calories, 1 g protein, 13 g carbohydrates, 0 g fat, 0 g saturated fat, 0 mg cholesterol, 17 mg sodium, 2 g dietary fiber

Exchanges: 1 fruit

Variation

Pineapple Sorbet: Replace the melon with 4 cups frozen, fresh, or canned in juice or water pineapple chunks.

Per serving: 67 calories, 1 g protein, 18 g carbohydrates, 0 g fat, 0 g saturated fat, 0 mg cholesterol, 1 mg sodium, 2 g dietary fiber

Exchanges: 1 fruit

Honeydew and Blueberry Freeze

1   *cup honeydew melon chunks*

2   *teaspoons fresh mint leaves*

2   *cups (16 ounces) fat-free plain Greek-style yogurt*

3   *tablespoons sugar or Splenda*

1   *cup blueberries*

Place the melon, mint, 1 cup of the yogurt, and 1 tablespoon of the sugar or Splenda into a blender and puree until smooth. Transfer the puree to a plastic container. Repeat with the blueberries, remaining 1 cup yogurt, and remaining 2 tablespoons sugar or Splenda and transfer to another plastic container.

Freeze the purees for 2 hours, stirring every 30 minutes to break up the ice crystals.

Remove the purees from the freezer a few minutes before serving. Spoon mounds of each frozen puree into 4 glass dessert cups or wine glasses. (If the purees are too firm to serve, microwave on medium power to soften slightly, for about 10 seconds.)

Makes 4 servings

Per serving: 138 calories, 8 g protein, 28 g carbohydrates, 0 g fat, 0 g saturated fat, 3 mg cholesterol, 118 mg sodium, 1 g dietary fiber

Exchanges: ½ milk, ½ fruit, ½ other carbohydrate

Desserts *and* Other Confections

The word *dessert* was originally used to describe food that was served after the table was cleared or "deserted" of everything else. While fruit was once a popular choice, now it's usually replaced by a sweeter course of strudels, crêpes, cannolis, soufflés, or one of the many other fabulous desserts featured throughout the book and in this chapter. Once again, you will find that these confections have been trimmed to allow for the diabetic diet. They still maintain their rich flavors and smooth, creamy textures thanks to cocoa powder, whole grain pastry flour, and the substitution of low-fat milk or yogurt for heavy cream.

Chocolate Soufflés

¼   cup unsweetened cocoa powder

2   tablespoons cornstarch

1   teaspoon ground cinnamon

¾   cup whole milk

½   cup reduced-calorie maple-flavored syrup

2   egg yolks, at room temperature

3   egg whites, at room temperature

½   teaspoon cream of tartar

Preheat the oven to 400°F. Coat six 6-ounce soufflé dishes or custard cups with cooking spray. Place on a baking sheet.

In a medium saucepan, whisk together the cocoa powder, cornstarch, and cinnamon. Whisk in the milk and maple syrup. Whisk over medium heat for 4 to 8 minutes, or until hot. Remove from the heat.

Place the egg yolks in a small bowl and whisk lightly. Slowly whisk in about ½ cup of the cocoa mixture. Pour into the saucepan and mix well.

Place the egg whites and cream of tartar in a large bowl. Using an electric mixer on high speed, beat until soft peaks form.

Gently stir about one-third of the egg whites into the cocoa mixture to lighten it. Fold in the remaining whites until no white streaks remain. Evenly divide among the prepared dishes.

Bake for 15 to 20 minutes, or until the soufflés are puffed and a knife inserted near the center comes out clean. Serve immediately.

Makes 6 servings

Per serving: 77 calories, 5 g protein, 11 g carbohydrates, 3 g fat, 1 g saturated fat, 75 mg cholesterol, 77 mg sodium, 1 g dietary fiber

Exchanges: ½ starch, ½ other carbohydrate, ½ very lean meat, ½ fat

Coffee Cup Soufflés

1	tablespoon butter, at room temperature
5	tablespoons granulated sugar
¼	cup cornstarch
3	tablespoons packed light brown sugar
3	tablespoons unsweetened cocoa powder
1½	teaspoons instant espresso powder
¼	teaspoon ground cinnamon
1¼	cups evaporated fat-free milk
2	teaspoons vanilla extract
6	egg whites, at room temperature
⅛	teaspoon salt

Preheat the oven to 400°F. Coat six 7-ounce ovenproof coffee cups, soufflé dishes, or custard cups with the butter. Dust evenly using 2 tablespoons of the granulated sugar. Place on a baking sheet.

In a medium saucepan, whisk together 2 tablespoons of the remaining granulated sugar, the cornstarch, brown sugar, cocoa powder, espresso powder, and cinnamon. Whisk in the milk.

Whisk over medium heat for 5 minutes, or until the mixture comes to a boil and thickens. Remove from the heat. Whisk in the vanilla extract. Place a sheet of plastic wrap directly onto the surface of the milk mixture to prevent a skin from forming.

Place the egg whites and salt in a large bowl. Using an electric mixer on high speed, beat until foamy. Gradually beat in the remaining 1 tablespoon granulated sugar until stiff, glossy peaks form.

Gently stir about one-third of the egg whites into the milk mixture to lighten it. Then pour the milk mixture over the beaten whites. Fold together until no white streaks remain. Evenly divide among the prepared cups.

Bake for 13 to 15 minutes, or until puffed and firm to the touch. Serve immediately.

Makes 6 servings

Per serving: 150 calories, 8 g protein, 24 g carbohydrates, 2 g fat, 1 g saturated fat, 7 mg cholesterol, 185 mg sodium, 1g dietary fiber

Exchanges: ½ starch, ½ milk, ½ other carbohydrate, ½ very lean meat, ½ fat

Peach Soufflé with Blueberries

1½	cups frozen peaches, thawed and patted dry
¼	cup sugar
2	egg yolks, at room temperature
1	tablespoon lemon juice
½	teaspoon ground nutmeg
5	egg whites, at room temperature
½	teaspoon cream of tartar
⅛	teaspoon ground cinnamon
½	cup blueberries

Preheat the oven to 350°F.

Place the peaches in a blender and process until smooth. Transfer to a medium bowl and mix in the sugar, egg yolks, lemon juice, and nutmeg.

Place the egg whites and cream of tartar in a large bowl. Using an electric mixer on high speed, beat until stiff peaks form.

Gently stir about one-third of the egg whites into the peach mixture to lighten it. Then pour the peach mixture over the beaten whites. Fold together until no white streaks remain.

Pour into a 1½-quart soufflé dish or baking dish and sprinkle with the cinnamon. Place the dish in a larger baking pan, then place on the bottom rack of the oven. Pour 1" of hot water into the outer pan.

Bake for 50 to 60 minutes, or until puffed and lightly browned. Serve immediately with the blueberries.

Makes 4 servings

Per serving: 140 calories, 6 g protein, 23 g carbohydrates, 3 g fat, 1 g saturated fat, 106 mg cholesterol, 74 mg sodium, 2 g dietary fiber

Exchanges: ½ fruit, 1 other carbohydrate, ½ lean meat, ½ fat

Blintz Soufflé

1 package (13 ounces) frozen apple, blueberry, or cherry blintzes (6 blintzes) *

3 eggs

1 cup reduced-fat sour cream

½ cup granulated sugar

¼ cup orange juice

1 teaspoon vanilla extract

2 tablespoons packed light brown sugar

Preheat the oven to 350°F. Line a 9" x 5" loaf pan with the frozen blintzes.

In a medium bowl, whisk together the eggs, sour cream, granulated sugar, orange juice, and vanilla extract. Pour over the blintzes. Sprinkle with the brown sugar.

Bake for 1 hour, or until the filling is set. Let stand for 5 minutes before cutting into slices.

Makes 10 servings

Per serving: 173 calories, 6 g protein, 24 g carbohydrates, 6 g fat, 3 g saturated fat, 100 mg cholesterol, 85 mg sodium, 0 g dietary fiber

Exchanges: 1½ other carbohydrate, ½ lean meat, 1 fat

Chocolate Cannolis

2 tablespoons + 1 teaspoon butter

16 square wonton skins

1 teaspoon ground cinnamon

1 container (16 ounces) whole milk ricotta cheese

½ cup confectioners' sugar

1 teaspoon vanilla extract

4 tablespoons miniature semisweet chocolate chips

Baking Tip: If you don't have cannoli molds, use the thick handle of a metal whisk or another ovenproof tube about ½" in diameter.

Preheat the oven to 400°F. Coat 2 large baking sheets with cooking spray.

In a small saucepan, melt 2 tablespoons of the butter and use to lightly brush both sides of a wonton skin. Sprinkle with a little cinnamon. Shape into a tube by curling opposite corners around a cannoli mold. Place, seam side down, on the prepared baking sheet. Repeat to make a total of 16 shells. (Work in batches, if necessary, according to how many molds you have.)

Bake for 7 minutes, or until lightly browned at the edges and set. Remove from the oven and let stand on a rack for 3 minutes, or until the shells have cooled on the molds and are crisp. Gently slide them onto the rack to cool completely.

In a large bowl, combine the ricotta, confectioners' sugar, and vanilla extract. Using an electric mixer on medium speed, beat well. Stir in 2 tablespoons of the chocolate chips. Cover and refrigerate until ready to serve.

Just before serving, spoon the ricotta mixture into a pastry bag fitted with a large tip. Pipe into the shells from both ends.

Place the remaining 2 tablespoons chocolate chips and 1 teaspoon butter in a small microwaveable bowl. Microwave on high power, stirring every 20 seconds, until the chocolate is almost melted. Stir until completely melted and smooth. Using a fork, drizzle over the cannolis.

Makes 16

Per cannoli: 101 calories, 4 g protein, 8 g carbohydrates, 6 g fat, 4 g saturated fat, 19 mg cholesterol, 58 mg sodium, 0 g dietary fiber

Exchanges: ½ other carbohydrate, ½ lean meat, 1 fat

Confetti Cannolis

1   container (16 ounces) whole milk ricotta cheese

½   cup + 1 tablespoon confectioners' sugar

1   teaspoon vanilla extract

¼   teaspoon almond extract

½   cup miniature candy-coated baking bits

8   prepared cannoli shells

In a large bowl, combine the ricotta, ½ cup of the confectioners' sugar, the vanilla extract, and almond extract. Using an electric mixer on medium speed, beat well. Stir in the baking bits.

Just before serving, spoon the ricotta mixture into a pastry bag fitted with a large tip. Pipe into the shells from both ends. Sprinkle with the remaining confectioners' sugar.

Makes 8

Per cannoli: 217 calories, 8 g protein, 23 g carbohydrates, 10 g fat, 6 g saturated fat, 30 mg cholesterol, 100 mg sodium, 0 g dietary fiber

Exchanges: ½ starch, 1 other carbohydrate, 1 lean meat, 1½ fat

Tiramisu

Photograph on page 65

½ cup hot tap water

2 tablespoons instant espresso powder

32 ladyfingers, split

3 egg whites, at room temperature

1 cup sugar

3 tablespoons cold water

¼ teaspoon cream of tartar

4 ounces mascarpone cheese

4 ounces reduced-fat cream cheese, at room temperature

1 tablespoon semisweet chocolate shavings

Baking Tip: If you don't have instant espresso powder, substitute 3 tablespoons instant coffee powder. Ladyfingers are delicate sponge cakes shaped like a wide finger and are available in most supermarkets. Mascarpone is a dense Italian triple-cream cheese made from cow's milk and is available in Italian markets and in some supermarkets.

Preheat the oven to 350°F.

In a small bowl, mix the hot water and espresso powder. Using a pastry brush, lightly brush the flat side of each ladyfinger with the mixture.

Bring about 2" of water to a simmer in a large saucepan. In a medium heatproof bowl that will fit over the saucepan, combine the egg whites, sugar, cold water, and cream of tartar. Place the bowl over the saucepan. Using an electric mixer on low speed, beat for 4 minutes. Increase the speed to high and beat for 4 minutes, or until very thick. Remove the bowl from the saucepan. Beat for another 4 minutes, or until the mixture is very light and fluffy.

Place the mascarpone and cream cheese in a large bowl. Using the same beaters, beat until creamy. Add 1 cup of the egg whites and beat until smooth. Gradually fold in the remaining egg whites.

Line the bottom of a 3-quart baking dish with 16 of the ladyfingers; top with one-quarter of the filling. Repeat 3 times to use all the ladyfingers and filling. Sprinkle with the chocolate.

Cover and refrigerate for at least 4 hours or up to 3 days before serving.

Makes 12 servings

Per serving: 354 calories, 9 g protein, 54 g carbohydrates, 12 g fat, 6 g saturated fat, 231 mg cholesterol, 136 mg sodium, 1 g dietary fiber

Exchanges: 3½ other carbohydrate, ½ lean meat, 2 fat

Ice Cream Jelly Roll

2	teaspoons + 1 cup whole grain pastry flour
1	teaspoon baking powder
¼	teaspoon salt
4	egg whites, at room temperature
¾	cup granulated sugar
4	egg yolks, at room temperature
1	teaspoon vanilla extract
1	tablespoon confectioners' sugar
1	quart fat-free chocolate ice cream, softened

Preheat the oven to 375°F. Coat a 15" x 11" jelly-roll pan with cooking spray. Dust with 2 teaspoons of the flour; tap out the excess.

In a small bowl, mix the remaining 1 cup flour, the baking powder, and salt.

Place the egg whites in a medium bowl. Using an electric mixer on medium speed, beat until frothy. Slowly beat in ½ cup of the granulated sugar until stiff peaks form.

Place the egg yolks, the remaining ¼ cup granulated sugar, and the vanilla extract in a large bowl. Using the same beaters, beat for 5 minutes, or until thick and lemon-colored.

Fold in one-third of the flour mixture and one-half of the egg whites. Repeat, beginning and ending with the flour.

Pour the batter into the prepared pan and smooth the top.

Bake for 8 minutes, or just until the top springs back when lightly touched in the center.

Place a clean dish towel on the kitchen counter and sprinkle evenly with the confectioners' sugar. Loosen the edges of the baked cake and immediately invert onto the towel. Starting from a short end, roll up the cake (and the towel). Cool completely on a rack.

Carefully unroll the cake and remove the towel. Spread the top of the cake with the ice cream. Roll up the cake. Wrap in plastic wrap or foil and freeze for at least 30 minutes.

Makes 12 servings

Per serving: 182 calories, 7 g protein, 36 g carbohydrates, 2 g fat, 1 g saturated fat, 74 mg cholesterol, 167 mg sodium, 1 g dietary fiber

Exchanges: ½ starch, 2 other carbohydrate, ½ lean meat, ½ fat

Zuccotto

1	container (32 ounces) low-fat vanilla yogurt
¼	cup slivered blanched almonds
1	package (13.6 ounces) fat-free pound cake
3	tablespoons orange juice
2	tablespoons sweet Marsala wine or orange juice
½	cup confectioners' sugar
1	ounce semisweet chocolate, finely chopped
1	envelope unflavored gelatin
¼	cup cold water
	Sliced strawberries (optional)

Line a sieve with a coffee filter or white paper towel and place over a deep bowl. Place the yogurt in the sieve. Cover with plastic wrap, refrigerate, and allow to drain for 4 hours, or until very thick. Discard the liquid in the bowl. Spoon the yogurt into a medium bowl.

Preheat the oven to 350°F. Place the almonds in a baking pan and toast for about 8 minutes, or until lightly browned. Chop.

Coat a deep 2-quart bowl with cooking spray. Line the bowl with plastic wrap. Cut the cake into twenty ¼"-thick slices. Place 1 slice in the center of the bottom of the bowl. Cut the remaining slices in half diagonally to form triangles. Arrange enough triangles around the inside of the bowl to cover completely, overlapping to fit.

In a cup, combine the orange juice and Marsala or additional orange juice. Brush lightly over the cake.

To the bowl with the drained yogurt, add the sugar, chocolate, and toasted almonds. Mix well.

In a small saucepan, sprinkle the gelatin over the cold water and let stand for 1 minute. Cook over low heat, stirring, for 2 to 3 minutes, or until the gelatin dissolves. Gradually whisk the gelatin mixture into the yogurt mixture, whisking constantly until it is completely incorporated.

Spoon the yogurt mixture into the bowl to cover the cake. Cover the yogurt mixture completely with the remaining cake slices. Brush the remaining orange juice mixture onto the cake slices. Cover with plastic wrap and chill for at least 3 hours, or overnight.

To serve, uncover and invert the zuccotto onto a platter. Remove the bowl and plastic wrap. Top with the strawberries (if using).

Makes 12 servings

Per serving: 210 calories, 7 g protein, 38 g carbohydrates, 4 g fat, 1 g saturated fat, 4 mg cholesterol, 161 mg sodium, 1 g dietary fiber

Exchanges: 2½ other carbohydrate, ½ very lean meat, ½ fat

Baking Tip: In Italian, zuccotto means *skullcap*; this impressive dessert was apparently named for its domed shape. Similar to a trifle, zuccotto is best if made the day before serving.

Cassata Siciliana

¼   cup water

¼   cup + ⅓ cup sugar

1   teaspoon rum extract

1   container (15 ounces) fat-free ricotta cheese

½   cup chopped mixed fruit

1   ounce semisweet chocolate, chopped

1   tablespoon grated orange rind

1   package (10 ounces) angel food cake

1   tablespoon unsweetened cocoa powder

Bring the water to a boil in a small saucepan. Add ¼ cup of the sugar and stir to dissolve. Stir in the rum extract and turn off the heat.

Line a 9" x 5" loaf pan with plastic wrap.

In a medium bowl, mix the ricotta and the remaining ⅓ cup sugar. Stir in the fruit, chocolate, and orange rind.

With a serrated knife, cut the angel food cake into ½"-thick slices. Line the bottom of the prepared pan with a layer of slices. Brush the slices with 2 tablespoons of the rum syrup. Spread with one-third of the ricotta filling. Repeat the layers twice.

Arrange the remaining slices of cake over the top and brush with the remaining syrup. Cover with plastic wrap and weigh down the cake with another loaf pan and a heavy weight or can.

Refrigerate for at least 15 minutes or overnight. To serve, invert the loaf pan onto a serving dish. Remove the plastic wrap. Dust with the cocoa powder.

Make 8 servings

Per serving: 227 calories, 5 g protein, 48 g carbohydrates, 3 g fat, 2 g saturated fat, 6 mg cholesterol, 291 mg sodium, 2 g dietary fiber

Exchanges: 1 fruit, 2½ other carbohydrate, 1 fat

Cheese Blintzes

⅔ cup fat-free milk

⅓ cup whole grain pastry flour

¼ cup liquid egg substitute

½ teaspoon baking powder

1½ cups low-fat sour cream

2 tablespoons honey

1 tablespoon grated orange rind

¼ teaspoon ground cinnamon

1 teaspoon canola oil

2 cups blueberries

1 cup applesauce

In a blender, combine the milk, flour, egg substitute, and baking powder. Blend until smooth, scraping down the sides of the container as needed.

Coat a small nonstick skillet with cooking spray. Place the pan over medium-high heat. Ladle in about 3 tablespoons batter and swirl it around to coat the bottom of the pan.

Cook the blintz for about 1 minute, or until the top is dry and the bottom is lightly browned. Flip the blintz out onto a rack or clean dish towel by turning the pan upside down. Continue making blintzes with the remaining batter. You should have 8.

In a small bowl, mix 1 cup of the sour cream, the honey, orange rind, and cinnamon.

Spoon 1 rounded tablespoon of the filling onto the middle of each blintz. Fold the bottom of the blintz over the filling. Then fold in the sides. Finish by rolling the whole thing up into a little pouch.

Coat a large nonstick skillet with cooking spray. Place over medium heat until hot. Add the oil and cook the blintzes for a few minutes on each side to lightly brown.

Serve topped with the blueberries, applesauce, and the remaining ½ cup sour cream.

Makes 8 servings

Per serving: 148 calories, 4 g protein, 19 g carbohydrates, 7 g fat, 4 g saturated fat, 18 mg cholesterol, 77 mg sodium, 2 g dietary fiber

Exchanges: ½ fruit, ½ other carbohydrate, 1½ fat

Kamut Crêpes with Cottage Cheese and Fruit

Crêpes

⅓ cup kamut flour

2 tablespoons white whole wheat flour or whole grain pastry flour

⅛ teaspoon salt

⅓ cup apple cider

½ cup + 2 tablespoons water

1 egg, lightly beaten

4 teaspoons butter, melted

Filling

1 cup small-curd 2% cottage cheese or ricotta cheese, at room temperature

2 pears, at room temperature, peeled and thinly sliced

¼ cup low-calorie maple syrup

To make the crêpes: In a large bowl, stir together the kamut flour and whole wheat flour or pastry flour, and salt.

In a small bowl, whisk together the apple cider, ½ cup of the water, egg, and 2 teaspoons of the butter. Whisk into the flour mixture to make a smooth batter. Add more water, 1 tablespoon at a time, if the batter is too thick.

Spread ½ teaspoon of the remaining butter in an 8" nonstick skillet over medium heat. Pour 3 tablespoons of batter into the skillet and tilt the skillet to coat the bottom in a thin layer (if the batter seems too thick, add 1 to 2 tablespoons of water). Cook the first side until lightly browned, about 1 minute. Using a spatula, turn and cook the second side for 30 to 60 seconds (the second side will look spotty). Slide the crêpe onto a plate and cover with foil to keep warm. Continue making crêpes in the same fashion, rebuttering the pan after every second crêpe, until all the butter and batter are used.

To make the filling and assemble: Place a crêpe on a plate, attractive side down. Arrange the cottage cheese or ricotta cheese and pear in a line ⅓ of the way from one edge. Roll up. Fill the remaining crêpes in the same manner. Serve drizzled with the syrup.

Makes 4 servings

Per serving: 213 calories, 12 g protein, 28 g carbohydrates, 7 g fat, 4 g saturated fat, 67 mg cholesterol, 381 mg sodium, 4 g dietary fiber

Exchanges: ½ starch, 1 fruit, 1 fat, 1 very lean meat

Cooking Tip: Crêpes cooked in butter brown beautifully. If you substitute cooking spray, increase the heat to medium-high, and the crêpes will brown moderately well.

Cherry-Cheese Crêpes

Crêpes

¾   *cup fat-free milk*

¼   *cup liquid egg substitute*

½   *teaspoon honey*

½   *cup whole grain pastry flour*

Filling

⅓   *cup fat-free cottage cheese*

⅓   *cup (2½ ounces) low-fat plain yogurt*

½   *teaspoon honey*

½   *teaspoon vanilla extract*

1   *cup pitted dark sweet cherries*

To make the crêpes: In a medium bowl, whisk together the milk, egg substitute, and honey. Whisk in the flour just until smooth.

Cover and let stand at room temperature for 2 hours. (This allows the flour particles to swell and soften to produce lighter crêpes.)

Coat a small nonstick skillet with cooking spray. Place over medium heat until a drop of water sizzles and evaporates upon contact.

Ladle in about 3 tablespoons batter and swirl it around to coat the bottom of the pan. Cook for 1 to 2 minutes, or until the edges begin to brown and the batter is set. Using a rubber spatula, loosen the edges and carefully flip the crêpe over. Cook the other side for 45 seconds. Transfer to a plate. Continue making crêpes with the remaining batter. You should have 8.

To make the filling: In a food processor, combine the cottage cheese, yogurt, honey, and vanilla extract. Process until smooth. Add the cherries and pulse until finely chopped but not pureed.

Spoon about 2 tablespoons of the filling onto the center of each crêpe. Roll up the crêpes and place them on dessert plates. Spoon a dollop of the remaining filling on top of each serving.

Makes 4 servings

Per serving: 185 calories, 15 g protein, 28 g carbohydrates, 2 g fat, 1 g saturated fat, 7 mg cholesterol, 239 mg sodium, 2 g dietary fiber

Exchanges: ½ starch, 1 milk, ½ very lean meat

Apple Clafouti

1	large McIntosh or Granny Smith apple, peeled, cored, and thinly sliced
¼	cup fresh or frozen cranberries
3	tablespoons honey
½	teaspoon ground cinnamon
1	can (12 ounces) fat-free evaporated milk
1	tablespoon olive oil
3	eggs, lightly beaten
1	teaspoon vanilla extract
⅔	cup unbleached flour
¼	cup sugar

Preheat the oven to 375°F. Spray a 9" glass pie plate with cooking spray.

Layer the apples in the bottom of the prepared pie plate to form a concentric circle (overlapping, if necessary). Strew the cranberries on top, then drizzle with the honey and sprinkle with ¼ teaspoon of the cinnamon.

In a food processor or blender, combine the milk, oil, eggs, vanilla extract, flour, sugar, and the remaining cinnamon. Blend until smooth and pour over the apples.

Bake for 40 minutes, or until puffy and golden. Serve warm or at room temperature.

Makes 8 servings

Per serving: 174 calories, 7 g protein, 29 g carbohydrates, 4 g fat, 1 g saturated fat, 81 mg cholesterol, 76 mg sodium, 1 g dietary fiber

Exchanges: ½ starch, ½ milk, ½ fruit, ½ other carbohydrate, ½ fat, ½ meat

Baking Tip: A clafouti is a dessert consisting of a layer of fruit topped with batter and baked.

Peach Clafouti

Photograph
on page 70

1	teaspoon + ½ cup granulated sugar
1⅓	cups whole milk
¾	cup whole grain pastry flour
3	eggs
2	tablespoons minced crystallized ginger
1	teaspoon vanilla extract
⅛	teaspoon salt
3	cups sliced peaches
2	tablespoons + 2 teaspoons confectioners' sugar

Preheat the oven to 400°F. Coat a 9" deep-dish pie plate with cooking spray. Dust with 1 teaspoon of the granulated sugar.

In a large bowl, mix the remaining ½ cup granulated sugar, the milk, flour, eggs, ginger, vanilla extract, and salt until smooth.

Pour half of the batter into the prepared pie plate.

In a medium bowl, mix the peaches and 2 tablespoons of the confectioners' sugar. Arrange the peaches in a pattern over the batter. Top with the remaining batter.

Bake for 50 minutes, or until puffed, browned, and firm. Cool on a rack for at least 20 minutes.

To serve, sprinkle with the remaining 2 teaspoons confectioners' sugar.

Makes 8 servings

Per serving: 173 calories, 5 g protein, 32 g carbohydrates, 3 g fat, 1 g saturated fat, 85 mg cholesterol, 9 mg sodium, 2 g dietary fiber

Exchanges: ½ starch, ½ fruit, 1 other carbohydrate, ½ lean meat, ½ fat

Cherry-Almond Clafouti

1	teaspoon + ½ cup granulated sugar
1⅓	cups whole milk
¾	cup whole grain pastry flour
3	eggs
¼	teaspoon almond extract
2	cups pitted sweet cherries
1½	teaspoons confectioners' sugar

Preheat the oven to 400°F. Coat a 9" deep-dish pie plate with cooking spray. Dust with 1 teaspoon of the granulated sugar.

In a large bowl, mix the remaining ½ cup granulated sugar, the milk, flour, eggs, and almond extract until smooth.

Pour half of the batter into the prepared pie plate. Add the cherries and then the remaining batter.

Bake for 40 minutes, or until puffed, browned, and firm. Cool on a rack for at least 20 minutes.

To serve, sprinkle with the confectioners' sugar.

Makes 6 servings

Per serving: 211 calories, 7 g protein, 35 g carbohydrates, 5 g fat, 2 g saturated fat, 115 mg cholesterol, 65 mg sodium, 2 g dietary fiber

Exchanges: ½ starch, ½ fruit, 1 other carbohydrate, ½ lean meat, 1 fat

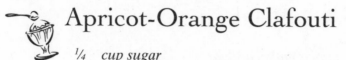

Apricot-Orange Clafouti

¼   *cup sugar*

1⅓   *cups 2% milk or unsweetened soy milk*

¾   *cup oat flour or whole grain pastry flour*

¼   *cup Splenda*

3   *eggs*

2   *teaspoons grated orange rind*

½   *teaspoon grated ginger*

½   *teaspoon vanilla extract*

2   *cups (about 10) pitted and sliced apricots*

¼   *teaspoon ground cinnamon*

Preheat the oven to 400°F. Coat a 9" deep-dish pie plate or quiche pan with cooking spray and dust with 1 teaspoon of the sugar.

In a large bowl, whisk together the milk, flour, remaining sugar, Splenda, eggs, orange rind, ginger, and vanilla extract.

Pour half of the batter into the prepared dish. Arrange the apricots evenly over the batter, then top with the remaining batter. Sprinkle with the cinnamon.

Bake for 40 minutes, or until puffed, browned, and firm. Cool on a rack for at least 15 minutes.

Makes 6 servings

Per serving: 173 calories, 7 g protein, 26 g carbohydrates, 5 g fat, 2 g saturated fat, 110 mg cholesterol, 58 mg sodium, 2 g dietary fiber

Exchanges: ½ starch, ½ fruit, ½ other carbohydrate, ½ fat, ½ meat

No-Bake Strawberry Dessert

1   *prepared angel food cake, cut into 1" cubes*

2   *packages (0.3 ounces each) sugar-free strawberry gelatin*

2   *cups boiling water*

1   *package (16–20 ounces) frozen unsweetened whole strawberries, thawed*

2   *cups 1% milk*

1   *package (1 ounce) sugar-free instant vanilla pudding mix*

8   *ounces reduced-fat frozen whipped topping, thawed*

Place the cake cubes in a 13" x 9" baking dish.

In a medium bowl, combine the gelatin and water and stir to dissolve. Stir in the strawberries. Pour over the cake cubes in the dish and gently press the cake down. Cover and refrigerate for 1 hour, or until set.

In another medium bowl, whisk together the milk and pudding mix for 2 minutes, or until slightly thickened. Spoon over the cake. Spread the whipped topping over the top. Cover and refrigerate until serving.

Makes 16 servings

Per serving: 121 calories, 4 g protein, 22 g carbohydrates, 2 g fat, 2 g saturated fat, 2 mg cholesterol, 242 mg sodium, 1 g dietary fiber

Exchanges: 1 other carbohydrate, ½ fat

Strawberry Shortcakes

Photograph
on page 67

2	cups (16 ounces) low-fat vanilla yogurt
2	cups whole grain pastry flour
4	tablespoons chilled butter, cut into small pieces
2	tablespoons packed light brown sugar
2	teaspoons baking powder
¼	teaspoon baking soda
⅔	cup + 1 tablespoon low-fat buttermilk
1	tablespoon + ⅓ cup granulated sugar
2	pints strawberries, sliced
3	tablespoons orange juice
1	teaspoon grated orange rind

Line a sieve with a coffee filter or white paper towel and place over a deep bowl. Place the yogurt in the sieve. Cover with plastic wrap, refrigerate, and allow to drain for 4 hours, or until very thick. Discard the liquid in the bowl.

Preheat the oven to 400°F. Coat a large baking sheet with cooking spray.

In a large bowl, combine the flour, butter, brown sugar, baking powder, and baking soda. Mix with your fingers to form crumbs. Add ⅔ cup of the buttermilk, stirring with a fork until the dough comes together.

Turn the dough out onto a lightly floured surface. Gently pat or roll to a ¾" thickness. Using a 3" round cutter or large glass, cut into 6 biscuits. (You may have to pat the dough scraps together to cut out all the biscuits.)

Place on the prepared baking sheet. Brush with the remaining 1 tablespoon buttermilk. Sprinkle with 1 tablespoon of the granulated sugar.

Bake for 12 minutes, or until golden. Cool on a rack for 10 minutes. Remove from the sheet and place on the rack to cool completely.

In a large bowl, mix the strawberries, orange juice, and the remaining ⅓ cup granulated sugar. Let stand for 10 minutes, stirring occasionally.

In a medium bowl, whisk together the drained yogurt and orange rind.

Split the biscuits crosswise in half. On dessert plates, layer the biscuits with berries in the center and on the top. Top with the yogurt.

Makes 6 servings

Per serving: 299 calories, 10 g protein, 48 g carbohydrates, 10 g fat, 6 g saturated fat, 25 mg cholesterol, 376 mg sodium, 6 g dietary fiber

Exchanges: 1 starch, 1 fruit, 1 other starch, 2 fat

HEALTH BONUS:
The strawberries alone in these shortcakes supply 69 milligrams of vitamin C, more than the Daily Value for this essential vitamin. In one study, Italian researchers gave 40 people with diabetes 1 gram of vitamin C every day. After 4 months, the people's abilities to use insulin had significantly improved. The scientists think this may be because vitamin C helps insulin penetrate cells.

Apple Strudel

Photograph on page 144

2   *Granny Smith or Golden Delicious apples, peeled, cored, and thinly sliced (about 3 cups)*

¼   *cup packed light brown sugar*

2   *tablespoons golden raisins*

½   *teaspoon ground cinnamon*

¼   *teaspoon ground nutmeg*

⅓   *cup plain dry bread crumbs*

¼   *cup granulated sugar*

12   *sheets (17" x 11" each) frozen whole wheat phyllo dough, thawed*

½   *cup apricot all-fruit preserves, warmed*

1   *tablespoon confectioners' sugar*

Preheat the oven to 400°F. Line a large baking sheet with parchment paper.

In a large bowl, mix the apples, brown sugar, raisins, cinnamon, and nutmeg.

In a small bowl, mix the bread crumbs and granulated sugar.

Place the phyllo on a dry kitchen counter and cover with plastic wrap and a clean damp towel to keep it from drying out. Remove 1 sheet, spread it flat, and mist with butter-flavored cooking spray. Sprinkle with 1 scant tablespoon of the crumb mixture. Repeat layering to use 4 more of the remaining phyllo sheets and about half of the crumb mixture. Top with 1 phyllo sheet and mist with the cooking spray.

Spread with ¼ cup of the preserves to within 1" of the edges. Spoon half of the apple mixture over the preserves. Fold 1" of each long edge over the apple mixture. Starting with the short edge, roll up as tightly as possible. Gently place the strudel, seam side down, on the prepared baking sheet. Mist the top with cooking spray.

Repeat to make 11 more strudels.

Using a sharp knife, make several slashes in the top of each strudel.

Bake for 15 minutes, or until crisp and golden brown. Sprinkle with the confectioners' sugar. Serve warm.

Makes 12 servings

Per serving: 138 calories, 2 g protein, 30 g carbohydrates, 1 g fat, 0 g saturated fat, 0 mg cholesterol, 121 mg sodium, 2 g dietary fiber

Exchanges: 1 starch, ½ fruit, ½ other carbohydrate

Ice Cream Sandwich

8   *low-fat graham crackers, any flavor*

¾   *cup fat-free frozen yogurt, any flavor, softened*

2   *teaspoons semisweet chocolate chips, melted*

Place the graham crackers on a work surface and spoon the yogurt evenly onto 4 of the crackers. Drizzle with the chocolate and top with the remaining crackers. Wrap in plastic wrap and freeze for 30 minutes, or until set.

Makes 4 servings

Per serving: 103 calories, 3 g protein, 19 g carbohydrates, 2 g fat, 1 g saturated fat, 1 mg cholesterol, 109 mg sodium, 1 g dietary fiber

Exchanges: ½ starch, ½ other carbohydrate

Variations

Mint Ice Cream Sandwiches: Use fat-free mint chocolate chip frozen yogurt and chocolate graham crackers.

Per serving: 77 calories, 2 g protein, 14 g carbohydrates, 1 g fat, 1 g saturated fat, 1 mg cholesterol, 72 mg sodium, 0 g dietary fiber

Exchanges: 1 other carbohydrate

Butter Pecan Ice Cream Sandwiches: Use fat-free butter pecan frozen yogurt with cinnamon graham crackers.

Per serving: 103 calories, 3 g protein, 10 g carbohydrates, 2 g fat, 1 g saturated fat, 1 mg cholesterol, 109 mg sodium, 1 g dietary fiber

Exchanges: ½ starch, ½ other carbohydrate

Index

Underscored page references indicate boxed text. **Boldfaced** page references indicate photographs.

Conversion Chart

These equivalents have been slightly rounded to make measuring easier.

Volume Measurements

U.S.	Imperial	Metric
¼ tsp	–	1 ml
½ tsp	–	2 ml
1 tsp	–	5 ml
1 Tbsp	–	15 ml
2 Tbsp (1 oz)	1 fl oz	30 ml
¼ cup (2 oz)	2 fl oz	60 ml
⅓ cup (3 oz)	3 fl oz	80 ml
½ cup (4 oz)	4 fl oz	120 ml
⅔ cup (5 oz)	5 fl oz	160 ml
¾ cup (6 oz)	6 fl oz	180 ml
1 cup (8 oz)	8 fl oz	240 ml

Weight Measurements

U.S.	Metric
1 oz	30 g
2 oz	60 g
4 oz (¼ lb)	115 g
5 oz (⅓ lb)	145 g
6 oz	170 g
7 oz	200 g
8 oz (½ lb)	230 g
10 oz	285 g
12 oz (¾ lb)	340 g
14 oz	400 g
16 oz (1 lb)	455 g
2.2 lb	1 kg

Length Measurements

U.S.	Metric
¼"	0.6 cm
½"	1.25 cm
1"	2.5 cm
2"	5 cm
4"	11 cm
6"	15 cm
8"	20 cm
10"	25 cm
12" (1')	30 cm

Pan Sizes

U.S.	Metric
8" cake pan	20 × 4 cm sandwich or cake tin
9" cake pan	23 × 3.5 cm sandwich or cake tin
11" × 7" baking pan	28 × 18 cm baking tin
13" × 9" baking pan	32.5 × 23 cm baking tin
15" × 10" baking pan	38 × 25.5 cm baking tin (Swiss roll tin)
1½ qt baking dish	1.5 liter baking dish
2 qt baking dish	2 liter baking dish
2 qt rectangular baking dish	30 × 19 cm baking dish
9" pie plate	22 × 4 or 23 × 4 cm pie plate
7" or 8" springform pan	18 or 20 cm springform or loose-bottom cake tin
9" × 5" loaf pan	23 × 13 cm or 2 lb narrow loaf tin or pâté tin

Temperatures

Fahrenheit	Centigrade	Gas
140°	60°	–
160°	70°	–
180°	80°	–
225°	105°	¼
250°	120°	½
275°	135°	1
300°	150°	2
325°	160°	3
350°	180°	4
375°	190°	5
400°	200°	6
425°	220°	7
450°	230°	8
475°	245°	9
500°	260°	–